INTERACTIVE MERIDIAN YOGA POSES
TO ASSIST IN LEARNING
TRADITIONAL CHINESE MEDICINE MERIDIANS
AND ESSENTIAL ACUPUNCTURE POINT CATEGORIES

Illustrated and Compiled by CINAMON KIMBROUGH, LAc, LMT

ADVISORS
BAHIA AL-SALIHI, DC, LAc, RYT and LISA ROSE, DC, RYT
JULIE KOTIW, DIBCN, DC, BS, CMT, CYT
MIDWEST COLLEGE OF ORIENTAL MEDICINE | RACINE CAMPUS
Derived from a Major Paper Assignment directed by Professor Robert Chelnick, B.S., Ph. D.

Contact us:
meridianninja@gmail.com | Phoenix, Az

Dedicated to my inspiring Meridian Ninjas
Nikko, Drake, Jay, Maritza and Julz
A,F,D and A
Susan and Spencer Tauck's Studios and Frog Sanctuary

Harris M. Kimbrough, Jr. D.D.S
Diane and Scott Kimbrough
Kristi Sharrenberg

TABLE OF CONTENTS

INTERACTIVE MERIDIAN YOGA POSES
TO ASSIST IN LEARNING
TRADITIONAL CHINESE MEDICINE MERIDIANS
AND ESSENTIAL ACUPUNCTURE POINT CATEGORIES

INTRODUCTION . . . . *Page 3*

THE TWELVE PRIMARY MERIDIANS . . . . *Page 6*

FIVE ELEMENT ANTIQUE POINTS . . . . *Page 19*

EXTRAORDINARY MASTER | COUPLE POINTS . . . . *Page 33*

SHU | MU | LUO | XI-CLEFT POINTS . . . . *Page 43*

IMPORTANT ACUPUNCTURE POINT CATEGORIES . . . . *Page 49*

INTRODUCTION

The average student reduces activity when attending college. They spend extra hours in the car, reading and studying, and possibly sitting at a position of employment. Within the text of The Yellow Emperor's Classic of Medicine in Chapter 2:

The Art of Life through the Four Seasons, this is unfavorable: … it is good to exercise, to stay open and unsuppressed (physically and emotionally)… stretching exercises to loosen up the tendons and muscles…stay active to prevent the pores from closing and qi stagnating and… breathing exercises to keep lung energy full, clean and quiet.

These acupuncture categories are critical in the learning of an acupuncture student. This handbook gives poses to physically experience the points and meridians.

This handbook is meant to apply the classic's philosophy and reduce stagnant study methods. These exercises may reduce the harm placed on the meridians by replacing an active method simultaneously while learning. You can use this color guide to assist you in remembering the color of the elements within TCM throughout this interactive handbook:

Daily stretching and exercises to enhance the qi is not new. Traditional Chinese Medicine has taught this philosophy for thousands of years. Furthermore, this is not Qi Gong or Tai Chi, the more Traditional Chinese Medicine approach to Exercise, yet you'll find these exercises overlap into many of those areas. This is also not by any means a complete study of yoga or physical therapy, although the postural exercises are derived from those practices. It is also a general entry-level study of acupuncture points. It is simply meant to complement a student's health and academic journey, with the goal of improving the quality of a student's life as they learn.

We hope by providing engaging graphics it will encourage learning in a visually pleasing technique as well as a kinesthetic technique.

Note: Many of the Postures are repeated when using the same meridian. This simplifies the memorization process. We can't possibly move just one meridian at a time in each exercise, so each pose clearly includes other meridians, as do all movements, yet we are using certain poses to signify only the one. We are also not diagnosing and treating according to a diagnosis, i.e. excess or deficiency. This is only a memorization of location.

Breathing: Inhaling fully into the belly with diaphragmatic breathing with full exhalation throughout the practice is encouraged. Where breathing and poses become challenging, it is advisable to alter pose to reduce tension. Use a chair or wall to enhance balance or shorten stretch. Use blocks or bolsters to support and align, as well as shorten stretch when necessary. Being patient, present and aware of your body are important to this practice. Know your limitations and respect them. Being mindful and remembering to breathe increases qi and blood. Damp, phlegm, stasis and stagnation (even emotion) are hindering and may create challenges, yet with dedication, we can move these obstructions and replace them with renewed qi and blood. As always, please consult with your primary caregiver before starting any of these exercises.

COLOR GUIDE FOR INTERACTIVE POSTURES

⚪🔘 METAL	◉ YUAN SOURCE	
🔘 WOOD	◉ XICLEFT	
⚫ WATER	◉ LUO	
⚫ FIRE	⚫ DU	
⚪🔘 EARTH	◉ CONCEPTION	

This book's paraphrased commentary and simplified illustrations are based off of:
Deadman, P., Al-Khafaji, M., & Baker, K. (2001). A Manual of Acupuncture
    East Sussex, England: Journal of Chinese Medicine Publications
    Special thanks to Peter Deadman. To get a more indepth look at Meridians and
    Acupuncture Points you can order this book, the online edition and/or mobile app at:

www.amanualofacupuncture.com

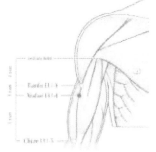

THE TWELVE PRIMARY MERIDIANS

5

LUNG MERIDIAN | ARM TAIYIN

ZANG ORGAN

Season: Autumn	Taste: Pungent	Tissue: Skin and Hair
Environmental Factor: Dryness	Sense Organ: Nose	Emotions: Grief and Melancholy

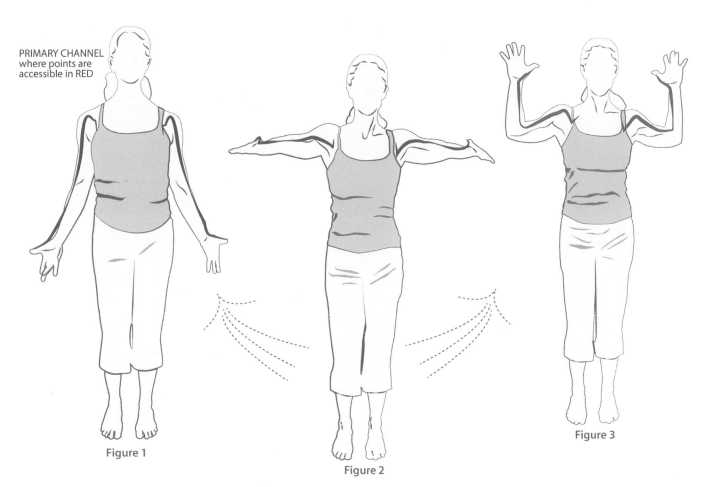

PRIMARY CHANNEL where points are accessible in RED

Figure 1

Figure 2

Figure 3

Figure 1. With feet, hips distance apart and fully planted evenly on the ground, stand tall. Take a deep inhalation. Open your chest, ribcage and shoulders while arms reach for the ground and the crown of head reaches for the sky. Feel the opening stretch of the **Arm Taiyin** Meridian.

Figure 2. On the exhale, open arms away from the body and stretch laterally until arms are level with shoulders. Let the **Grief** and **Melancholy** go allowing the lungs to expel stagnant qi. Continue breath in this manner. Sing the note **Shang** and envision the color **White** as it gleams and shines off of **Metal.**

Figure 3. Inhale deeply while bringing elbows into a 90° angle like cactus arms in a **Dry** desert. Exhale pressing scapula muscles medially and inferiorly together. Hold pose for the **count of 11** while breathing easily. Envision a **Zang** organ producing and storing vital substances in the lung. The lung qi is most abundant from **3am-5am**.

Lung and Large Intestine Meridians are Interiorly/Exteriorly paired
Six Channel pairing with the Leg Taiyin Spleen Meridian
Functions: • Governs qi • Controls respiration • Controls ascending and descending • Regulates the water passages • Controls the skin and body hair • Opens into the nose

♩ SHANG | WHITE

METAL

11

ACUPUNCTURE POINTS
Use count in pose to memorize.

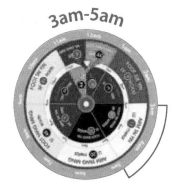

3am-5am

LARGE INTESTINE MERIDIAN | ARM YANGMING

Season: Autumn	Taste: Pungent	Tissue: Skin and Hair
Environmental Factor: Dryness	Sense Organ: Nose	Emotions: Grief and Melancholy

FU ORGAN

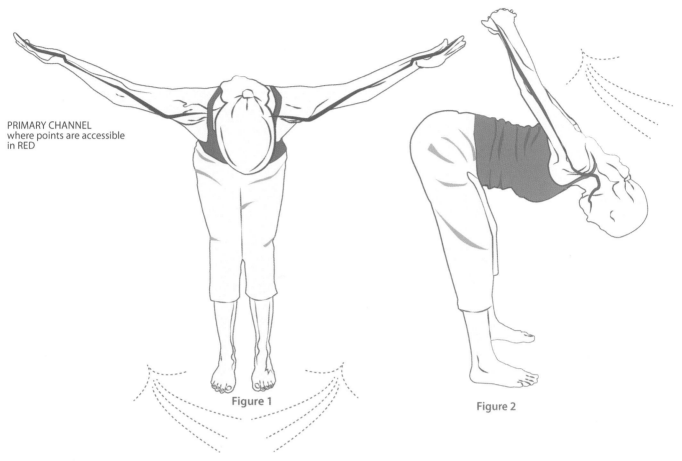

PRIMARY CHANNEL
where points are accessible
in RED

Figure 1

Figure 2

Figure 1. With slightly bended knees, fold forward while swinging arms out to the sides, resembling a swan dive, stretching to encompass the **Arm Yangming** meridian. Hold pose for a **count of 1-10,** breathing with ease. Sing the note **Shang** and envision the color **White** as it gleams and shines off of **Metal.**

Figure 2. If possible, clasp hands or clasp a towel/strap with both hands extending backwards toward the sky. Open the front of shoulders where the tension of **Grief and Melancholy** reside, allowing the circulation to irrigate any **Dry** vessels. Hold pose for a **count of 11-20** breathing with ease. Envision a **Fu** organ emptying and filling. The large intestine qi is most abundant from **5am-7am**.

♩ SHANG | WHITE

Large Intestine and lung are Interiorly/Exteriorly paired
Six Channel pairing with the Leg Yangming Stomach Meridian
Function: • Receive waste material via the Small Intestine, it absorbs its fluid content and excretes the rest The points are used to treat: • Yangming disorders; painful obstruction hemiplegia, paralysis because the yangming meridians are full of qi and blood

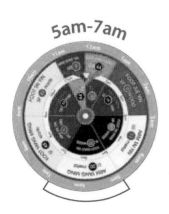

5am-7am

METAL

20

ACUPUNCTURE POINTS
Use count in pose to memorize.

STOMACH MERIDIAN | LEG YANGMING

FU ORGAN			
	Season: Late Summer	Taste: Sweet	Tissue: Muscle
	Environmental Factor: Damp	Sense Organ: Mouth	Emotions: Worry

Figure 1

Figure 2

PRIMARY CHANNEL
where points are accessible
in RED

Figure 3

Figure 1. Gently come down onto all fours and move into a bended-knee supported push-up position, feeling strength building within the **Leg Yangming** Meridian. Hold pose for a **count of 1-20,** breathing with ease.

Figure 2. Gently release the stomach and chest down to floor. Hold for the **count 21-25,** breathing easily. On an inhalation, raise the chest and allow the upper back to engage with scapular muscles, and shoulders back. Feel the stretch in the neck, chest and below the ribcage. Hold this pose for the **count of 26-40,** breathing with ease. State or mentally say the note **Gong** and envision the color **Yellow.**

Figure 3. Reaching behind with both arms and lifting legs with a full-body extension, allow the front body to stretch as if soaring in the sky without a **Worry** in the world, draining any **Damp** stagnation from sitting. Hold this pose for the **count of 41-45** breathing with ease. Release and rest all limbs and head on floor. Envision a **Fu** organ emptying and filling in the stomach. The stomach qi is most abundant from **7am-9am**.

Stomach and Spleen Meridians are Interiorly/Exteriorly paired
Six Channel pairing with the Arm Yangming Large Intestine Meridian
Functions: • Controls the rotting and ripening of food • Controls the descending and the first stage of the digestion of fluids • Yangming disorders; painful obstruction hemiplegia, paralysis because the yangming channels are full of qi and blood

GONG   YELLOW

EARTH
45
ACUPUNCTURE POINTS
Use count in pose to memorize.

7am-9am

SPLEEN MERIDIAN | LEG TAIYIN

Season: Late Summer	Taste: Sweet	Tissue: Muscle
Environmental Factor: Damp	Sense Organ: Mouth	Emotions: Worry

ZANG ORGAN

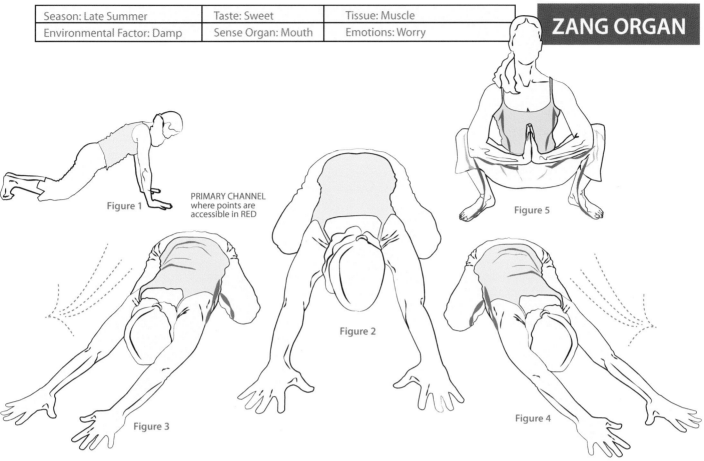

PRIMARY CHANNEL where points are accessible in RED

Figure 1

Figure 2

Figure 3

Figure 4

Figure 5

Figure 1. Return to a bended-knee supported push-up position.

Figure 2. While bringing the big toes together, expand knees to a comfortable yoga-mat distance apart. Reach forward with both arms with a deep inhalation. On the exhale, elongate the back, allowing the upper body to sink deeply into the floor, resting the forehead on the ground. Let **Worrying** thoughts seep into the **Earth**. Feel the lengthening stretch of the **Leg Taiyin** Meridian through the inner leg and intercostal muscles. Hold pose for a **count of 1-10,** breathing with ease. Sing the note **Gong** and envision the color **Yellow.**

Figure 3. Lift body slightly on a deep inhalation and walk hands over to the right. On a strong exhalation, sink back into the floor while releasing forehead to the **Earth**. Feel the lengthening of the inner legs and the left lateral intercostals with a **count of 11-21,** breathing with ease and releasing **Worrying** thoughts.

Figure 4. Walk hands to the center and repeat Figure 2, then Figure 3 on left side. State or mentally envision a **Zang** organ producing and storing vital substances in the spleen. The spleen qi is most abundant from **9am-11am.**

Figure 5. If you are prepared for more of a challenge, push up into a squat position and with hands in prayer position, feel a strengthening in the **Leg Taiyin** Meridian.

♩ GONG   YELLOW

9am-11am

EARTH
21
ACUPUNCTURE POINTS
Use count in pose to memorize.

Spleen and Stomach Meridians are Interiorly/Exteriorly paired

Six Channel pairing with the Arm Taiyin Lung Meridian

Functions:
- Transportation and transformation of solids and liquids
- Digestion, the production of qi and blood, intestinal function and the release of fluid
- Controls the blood, production of and containment of blood
- Muscles and the four limbs
- Sense of taste
- Controls the raising of qi

HEART MERIDIAN | ARM SHAOYIN

ZANG ORGAN

Season: Summer	Taste: Bitter	Tissue: Vessel
Environmental Factor: Heat	Sense Organ: Tongue	Emotions: Joy

PRIMARY CHANNEL where points are accessible in RED

Figure 1

Figure 2

Figure 3

Figure 1. Return to a bent-knee supported push-up position. Take a deep inhalation.

Figure 2. On the exhalation, keep right knee bent and slide foot posteriorly. Plant right arm directly under shoulder. Balance the body, increasing resistance through medial arm. Feel the strength and **Heat** build in the **Arm Shaoyin Meridian.** Open side body with inhalation and lift left arm to the sky. Outstretch the left leg, elongated at a side angle with an expression of **Joy.** Hold the pose for a **count of 9** and breathe and exhale within the intercostal muscles.

Figure 3. Release balance arm and bring side body up. Reach right arm to sky while lowering left arm to outstretched leg. Sing the note **Zheng** and envision the color **Red.** State or mentally envision a **Zang** organ producing and storing vital substances in the heart. The heart qi is abundant from **11am-1pm.** Repeat with opposite side.

♪ ZHENG   RED

Heart and Small Intestine Meridians are Interiorly/Exteriorly paired
Six Channel pairing with the Leg Shaoyin Kidney Meridian
Functions • Governs blood and vessels • Houses the spirit • Opens to the tongue • Governs sweating • Manifests in the complexion

FIRE

9

ACUPUNCTURE POINTS
Use count in pose to memorize.

11am-1pm

SMALL INTESTINE MERIDIAN | ARM TAIYANG

Season: Summer	Taste: Bitter	Tissue: Vessel
Environmental Factor: Heat	Sense Organ: Tongue	Emotions: Joy

FU ORGAN

Figure 1

Figure 2

Figure 1. Return to hands and knees on all fours. With deep inhalation, lift the right arm to the sky opening ribcage and extending lateral arm while building resistance in the posterior deltoid. On the exhalation, feel the **Arm Taiyang Meridian,** while building **Heat** in the posterior shoulder on the elevated arm and strengthening the opposing balancing arm. Hold the pose for a **count of 1- 9** and breathe deep into the intercostals.

Figure2. Take a deep inhalation and on the next exhalation, release the arm with **Joy** and thread right arm between left knee and left arm. Rest head and shoulder on the floor. Breathe into the organs and ribcage and hold pose for the **count of 10-19**. Sing the note **Zheng** and envision the color **Red.** Envision a **Fu** organ emptying and filling in the small intestine. The small intestine qi is most abundant from **1pm-3pm**.

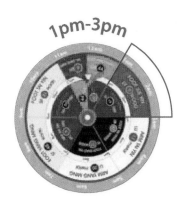

1pm-3pm

♩ ZHENG   RED

FIRE

19

ACUPUNCTURE POINTS
Use count in pose to memorize.

Small Intestine and Heart Meridians are Interiorly/Exteriorly paired

Six Channel pairing with the Leg Taiyang Urinary Bladder

Functions
- Organ function receives, transforms and separates fluids
- Element of Fire Meridian as a connector between heart and urinary bladder, clears heat and reduces fever
- Transforms phlegm and clears heart zang (mania)

URINARY BLADDER MERIDIAN | LEG TAIYANG

FU ORGAN	Season: Winter	Taste: Salty	Tissue: Bones
	Environmental Factor: Cold	Sense Organ: Ears	Emotions: Fear

Figure 1

Figure 2

Figure 3

Figure 1. Return to hands and knees.
Figure 2. On the inhalation, fold forward and release head to the floor. Let arms relax next to shins. With a deep exhale and soft spine, gently roll the neck. Feel expansion in the erector spinae muscles, suboccipital muscles and top of the cranium muscles, encompassing a stretch within the upper **Leg TaiYang** Meridian. Hold pose for the **count of 1-30,** breathing with ease. Sing the note **Yu** and envision the color **Black** like being in deep **Water.**

Figure 3. Return to hands and knees. Lengthen arms as far as possible and extend. Open shoulders with deep inhalation. With slight bend to the knee, lift the sacrum to the sky and press chest to thighs while exhaling into the full stretch of the **Leg TaiYang** Meridian as you flex your armor to conquer **Fear** as a warrior. Straighten first one knee by pressing one heel down to the floor, and then the other. Hold for the **count of 31-67,** breathing with ease. Breathe easily and state or mentally envision a **Zang** organ producing and storing vital substances in the urinary bladder. The urinary bladder qi is most abundant in the urinary bladder from **5pm-7pm**.

Urinary Bladder and Kidney Meridians are Interiorly/Exteriorly paired
Six Channel pairing with the Arm Taiyang Small Intestine Meridian
Functions: • Stores fluid • Converts the waste into urine for excretion via its qi's ability to transform Meridian treatment not usually used for treating urinary problems but are used to treat: • Eliminates both exterior and interior wind from the body (longest and most superficial meridian of the body) • Marrow disorders mania and epilepsy • Shu points treat organ and a variety of disorders

♩ YU   BLACK

WATER
67

ACUPUNCTURE POINTS
Use count in pose to memorize.

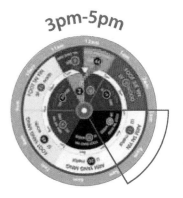

3pm-5pm

KIDNEY MERIDIAN | LEG SHAOYIN

Season: Winter	Taste: Salty	Tissue: Bones
Environmental Factor: Cold	Sense Organ: Ears	Emotions: Fear

ZANG ORGAN

PRIMARY CHANNEL
where points are
accessible in RED

Figure 1

Figure 2

Figure 1. While in Urinary Bladder pose, draw the left foot up to the sky while building strength at the ball of the right foot at Acupuncture point KD 1. Take a deep inhalation and look between your hands. On the exhalation, bring left foot between your hands.

Figure 2. Inhale while lifting torso upwards. As if pulling a bucket from the well full of **Water,** lift arms up to neck and exhale. Extend arms on both sides. Feel the strength rise in the **Leg Shaoyin** Meridian, from the feet up the inner leg and rising through the core body.

Hold pose for a **count of 27,** breathing with ease. Sing the note **Yu** and envision the color **Black** from being in deep **Water** conquering **Fear** with the strength of a warrior. Envision a **Zang** organ producing and storing vital substances in the kidney. The kidney qi is most abundant from **5pm-7pm**. Repeat on the opposite side.

♩ YU   **BLACK**

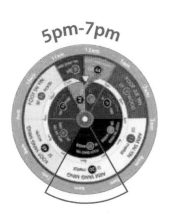
5pm-7pm

WATER
27

ACUPUNCTURE POINTS
Use count in pose to memorize.

Kidney and Urinary Bladder Meridians are Interiorly/Exteriorly paired

Six Channel pairing with the Arm Shaoyin Heart Meridian

Functions:
- Stores essence and dominates reproduction, growth and development
- Produces marrow, fills the brain, dominates bones and assists production of blood
- Dominates water
- Controls the reception of qi
- Opens into the ears and dominates the anus and urethra

13

PERICARDIUM MERIDIAN | ARM JUEYIN

ZANG ORGAN

Season: Summer	Taste: Bitter	Tissue: Vessel
Environmental Factor: Heat	Sense Organ: Tongue	Emotions: Joy

PRIMARY CHANNEL
where points are
accessible in RED

Figure 1

Figure 2

Figure 3

Figure 1. Return to a bent-knee supported push-up position. Take a deep inhalation.

Figure 2. On the exhalation, relax the whole body to the floor. Place a pillow or block beneath head and expand arms in a full wing span. Find your center within the sternum on the floor and experience the expansion of the arms in the **Arm Jueyin Meridian.**

Figure 3. Inhale deep within the chest cavity. Open side body with left arm up to the sky with an expression of **Joy.** Exhale while reaching for the **Fire** and **Heat** of the sun, keeping the right arm in its original position. Hold the pose for a **count of 9** and breathe deep into the intercostal muscles.

Return to all fours and repeat Figure 2 and 3 on the left side. Envision the color **Red.** Envision a **Zang** organ producing and storing vital substances in the pericardium to protect the heart. The pericardium qi is most abundant from **7pm-9pm.**

Pericardium and San Jiao Meridians are Interiorly/Exteriorly paired.
Six Channel pairing with the Leg Jueyin Liver Meridian.
Functions • Membrane surrounding the heart, protects the heart Treats Disorders of the • Chest: Heart, Lung Disharmony • Upper and Middle Jiao disorders due to Liver Qi stagnation • Disorders of the Stomach • Febrile diseases (nutritive and blood levels)

RED

FIRE
9

ACUPUNCTURE POINTS
Use count in pose to memorize.

7pm-9pm

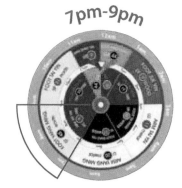

SAN JIAO MERIDIAN | ARM SHAOYANG

Season: Summer	Taste: Bitter	Tissue: Vessel
Environmental Factor: Heat	Sense Organ: Tongue	Emotions: Joy

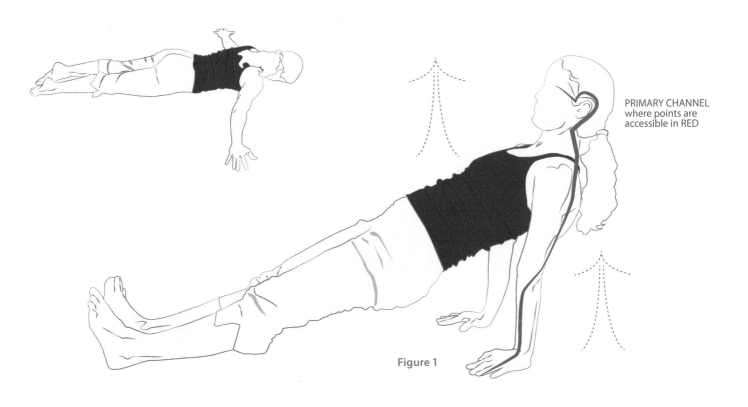

PRIMARY CHANNEL
where points are
accessible in RED

Figure 1

Figure 1. Roll over on to your back and come to a straight-legged seated pose. On a deep inhalation, place hands palm-side down and with an intentional full body lift and exhalation push torso up with the strength of the posterior and lateral areas of your arms. Feel the **Heat** building a **Fire** in the **Arm Shaoyang Meridian**. Hold the pose for a **count of 23** and breathe deep into all three Jiaos (Burners), to include **Upper Burner:** Lung, Pericardium and Heart. **Middle Burner:** Liver, Spleen and Stomach. **Lower Burner**: Large Intestine, Small Intestine, Kidney, Urinary Bladder.

Relax back to the floor and experience **Joy** as you envision the color **Red.** Envision a **Fu** organ emptying and filling in the San Jiao Meridian. The San Jiao qi is most abundant encompassing all three burners: upper, lower and middle from **9pm-11pm.**

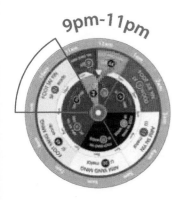

9pm-11pm

RED

FIRE
23

ACUPUNCTURE POINTS
Use count in pose to memorize.

San Jiao and Pericardium Meridians are Interiorly/Exteriorly paired
Six Channel pairing with the Leg Shaoyang Gall Bladder Meridian
Functions • Pivots between exterior and interior • Encompasses the Three Jiaos (Triple Burner) Treats Disorders • Headache • Benefits the ears • Reduces Fever (defensive and qi) • Regulates Vomiting and Constipation

GALL BLADDER MERIDIAN | LEG SHAOYANG

FU ORGAN

Season: Spring	Taste: Sour	Tissue: Tendons
Environmental Factor: Wind	Sense Organ: Eyes	Emotions: Anger

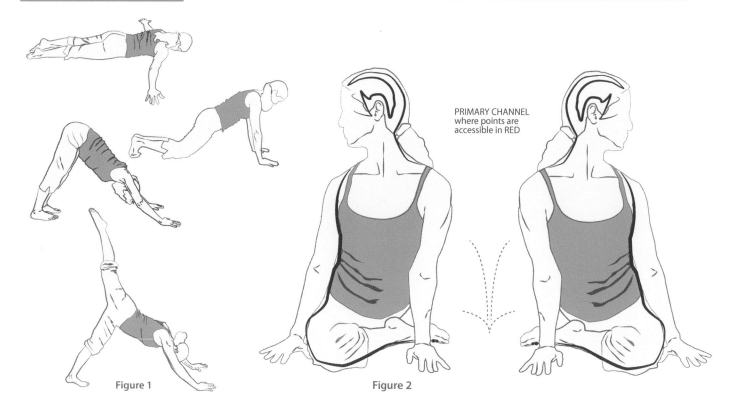

PRIMARY CHANNEL where points are accessible in RED

Figure 1

Figure 2

Figure 1. Come back to belly and into Urinary Bladder position. With a deep inhalation, bring right leg up to the sky.

Figure 2. On exhalation, bring right leg forward between arms and release right knee slightly in front of the pelvis with outer shin pressing on the floor and left leg straight behind. Take a deep inhalation and gently sit deep into the hip, while keeping both sides of hips level. Twist the upper body to the left while exhaling the **Wind** out of the body. Feel the lengthening and stretch of the **Leg Shao Yang** Meridian through the lateral leg, buttock, side body, lateral neck and head. Hold pose for a **count of 44,** breathing with ease.

Sing the note **Jiao** and envision the color **Green** in a **Wood**ed forest in the **Spring**.

Figure 3. Come onto hands and knees. Rest a few breaths and wiggle hips to release any tension. Repeat Figures 1 and 2 on the right side with left leg straightened behind you. Hold pose for a **count of 44,** breathing with ease. Envision a **Fu** organ emptying and filling in the Gall Bladder. The Gall Bladder qi is most abundant from **11pm-1am.**

Gall Bladder and Liver Meridians are Interiorly/Exteriorly paired
Six Channel pairing with the Arm Tai Yang San Jiao Meridian
Functions: • Stores and excretes bile • Rules courage, decision making, and judgment • Treats disorders of the liver such as: eyes and ears especially disorders with wind-heat or LV/GB channel heat also hypochondrial and sinew pain

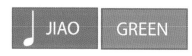

JIAO   GREEN

WOOD

44

ACUPUNCTURE POINTS
Use count in pose to memorize.

11pm-1am

LIVER MERIDIAN | LEG JUEYIN

Season: Spring	Taste: Sour	Tissue: Tendons
Environmental Factor: Wind	Sense Organ: Eyes	Emotions: Anger

PRIMARY CHANNEL where points are accessible in RED

Figure 1

Figure 2

Figure 3

Figure 1. When coming out of Gall Bladder pose, release the straight leg from behind and bring it comfortably to the front. Straighten out to the side with toes pointed and keep right leg folded.

Figure 2. On a deep inhalation, bring right hand to knee and grasp while reaching left arm out of the torso and to the sky. When rib cage is fully extended, slightly angle side body to the left, while exhaling the **Wind** out of the body. Feel the lengthening and stretch of the **Leg Jueyin**

Meridian from the big toe, inner ankle, medial thigh, and the groin up to the intercostal muscles beneath the breast. Hold pose for a **count of 14,** breathing deep into the diaphragm. Sing the note **Jiao** and envision the color **Green** in the **Woods**.

Figure 3. Shake out legs and reverse the straight leg to the right and repeat Figure 2 on the opposite side. Envision a **Zang** organ producing and storing vital substances in the Liver Meridian. The Liver qi is most abundant from **1am-3am**.

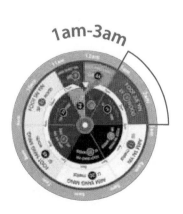

1am-3am

♩ JIAO   GREEN

WOOD

14

ACUPUNCTURE POINTS
Use count in pose to memorize.

Liver and Gall Bladder Meridians are Interiorly/Exteriorly paired
Six Channel pairing with the Arm Jueyin Pericardium Meridian
Functions: • Stores the blood • Spreads and maintains the free flow of the qi • Dominates the sinews • Opens into the eyes • Manifests in the nails

NOTES:

FIVE ELEMENT ANTIQUE POINTS

19

LUNG ANTIQUE POINTS

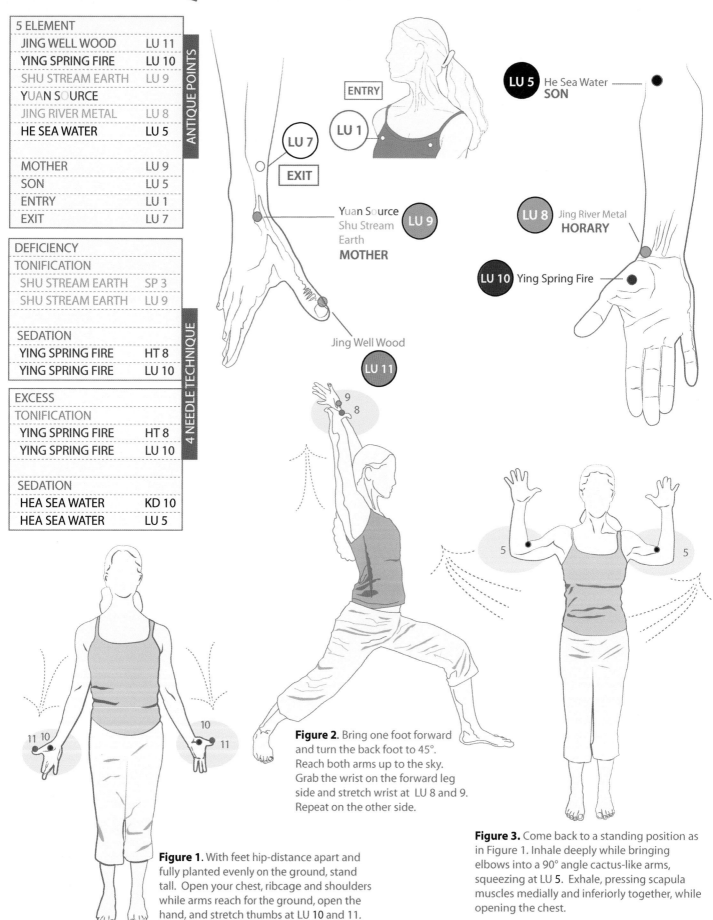

5 ELEMENT	
JING WELL WOOD	LU 11
YING SPRING FIRE	LU 10
SHU STREAM EARTH	LU 9
YUAN SOURCE	
JING RIVER METAL	LU 8
HE SEA WATER	LU 5
MOTHER	LU 9
SON	LU 5
ENTRY	LU 1
EXIT	LU 7

ANTIQUE POINTS

DEFICIENCY	
TONIFICATION	
SHU STREAM EARTH	SP 3
SHU STREAM EARTH	LU 9
SEDATION	
YING SPRING FIRE	HT 8
YING SPRING FIRE	LU 10

EXCESS	
TONIFICATION	
YING SPRING FIRE	HT 8
YING SPRING FIRE	LU 10
SEDATION	
HEA SEA WATER	KD 10
HEA SEA WATER	LU 5

4 NEEDLE TECHNIQUE

Figure 1. With feet hip-distance apart and fully planted evenly on the ground, stand tall. Open your chest, ribcage and shoulders while arms reach for the ground, open the hand, and stretch thumbs at LU **10** and **11**.

Figure 2. Bring one foot forward and turn the back foot to 45°. Reach both arms up to the sky. Grab the wrist on the forward leg side and stretch wrist at LU 8 and 9. Repeat on the other side.

Figure 3. Come back to a standing position as in Figure 1. Inhale deeply while bringing elbows into a 90° angle cactus-like arms, squeezing at LU **5**. Exhale, pressing scapula muscles medially and inferiorly together, while opening the chest.

LARGE INTESTINE ANTIQUE POINTS

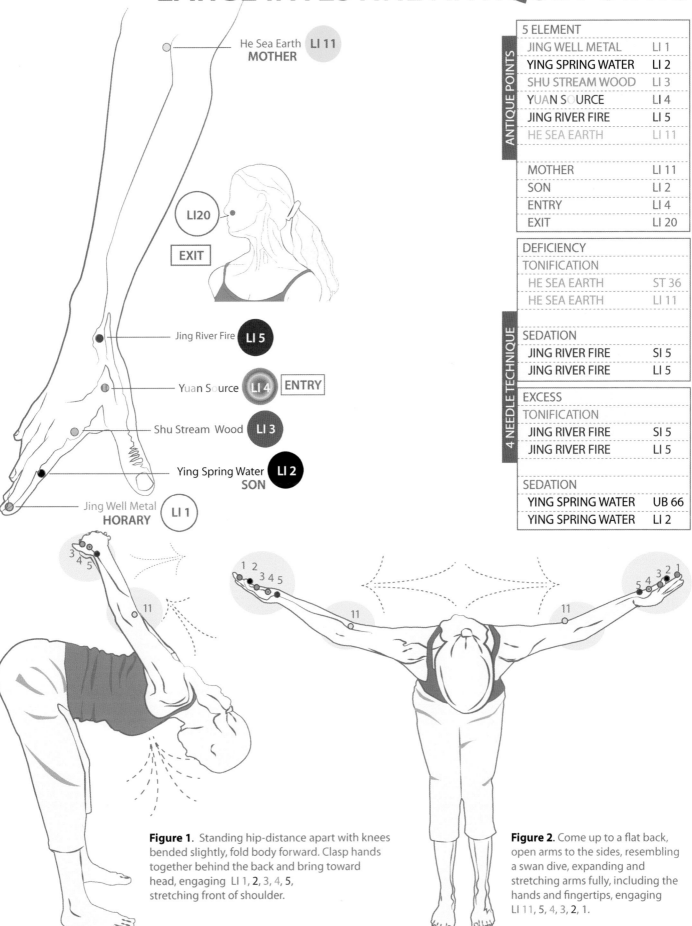

He Sea Earth **LI 11**
MOTHER

LI20

EXIT

Jing River Fire **LI 5**

Yuan Source **LI 4** **ENTRY**

Shu Stream Wood **LI 3**

Ying Spring Water **LI 2**
SON

Jing Well Metal **LI 1**
HORARY

5 ELEMENT	
JING WELL METAL	LI 1
YING SPRING WATER	LI 2
SHU STREAM WOOD	LI 3
YUAN SOURCE	LI 4
JING RIVER FIRE	LI 5
HE SEA EARTH	LI 11
MOTHER	LI 11
SON	LI 2
ENTRY	LI 4
EXIT	LI 20

DEFICIENCY	
TONIFICATION	
HE SEA EARTH	ST 36
HE SEA EARTH	LI 11
SEDATION	
JING RIVER FIRE	SI 5
JING RIVER FIRE	LI 5

EXCESS	
TONIFICATION	
JING RIVER FIRE	SI 5
JING RIVER FIRE	LI 5
SEDATION	
YING SPRING WATER	UB 66
YING SPRING WATER	LI 2

ANTIQUE POINTS

4 NEEDLE TECHNIQUE

Figure 1. Standing hip-distance apart with knees bended slightly, fold body forward. Clasp hands together behind the back and bring toward head, engaging LI 1, 2, 3, 4, 5, stretching front of shoulder.

Figure 2. Come up to a flat back, open arms to the sides, resembling a swan dive, expanding and stretching arms fully, including the hands and fingertips, engaging LI 11, 5, 4, 3, 2, 1.

STOMACH ANTIQUE POINTS

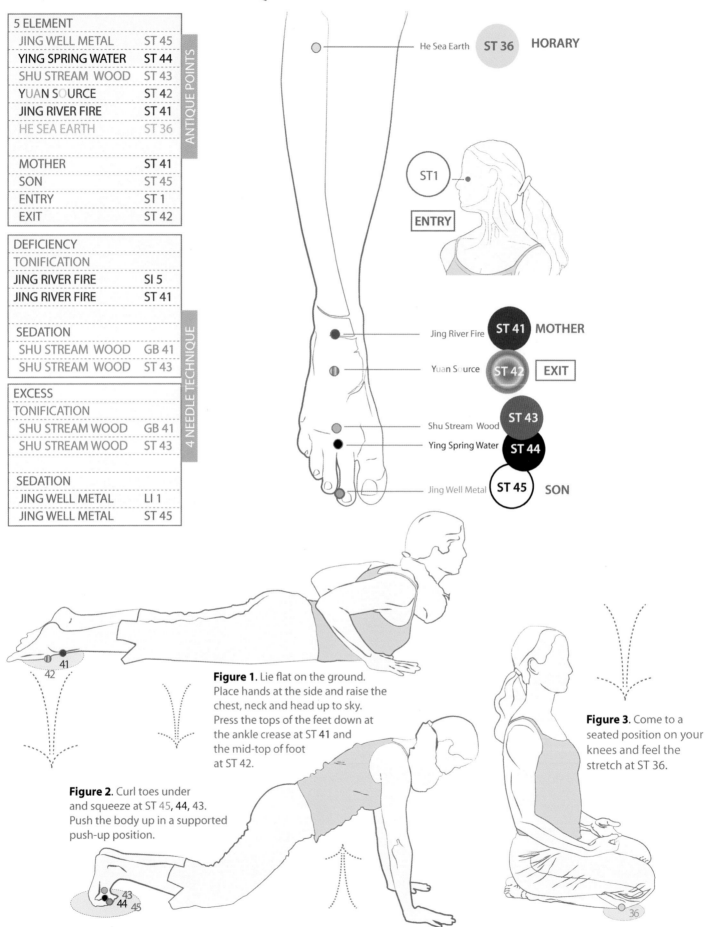

5 ELEMENT	
JING WELL METAL	ST 45
YING SPRING WATER	ST 44
SHU STREAM WOOD	ST 43
YUAN SOURCE	ST 42
JING RIVER FIRE	ST 41
HE SEA EARTH	ST 36
MOTHER	ST 41
SON	ST 45
ENTRY	ST 1
EXIT	ST 42

ANTIQUE POINTS

DEFICIENCY	
TONIFICATION	
JING RIVER FIRE	SI 5
JING RIVER FIRE	ST 41
SEDATION	
SHU STREAM WOOD	GB 41
SHU STREAM WOOD	ST 43

EXCESS	
TONIFICATION	
SHU STREAM WOOD	GB 41
SHU STREAM WOOD	ST 43
SEDATION	
JING WELL METAL	LI 1
JING WELL METAL	ST 45

4 NEEDLE TECHNIQUE

He Sea Earth **ST 36** HORARY

ST1 ⟶ **ENTRY**

Jing River Fire **ST 41** MOTHER

Yuan Source **ST 42** **EXIT**

Shu Stream Wood **ST 43**

Ying Spring Water **ST 44**

Jing Well Metal **ST 45** SON

Figure 1. Lie flat on the ground. Place hands at the side and raise the chest, neck and head up to sky. Press the tops of the feet down at the ankle crease at ST 41 and the mid-top of foot at ST 42.

42 41

Figure 2. Curl toes under and squeeze at ST 45, 44, 43. Push the body up in a supported push-up position.

43 44 45

Figure 3. Come to a seated position on your knees and feel the stretch at ST 36.

36

SPLEEN ANTIQUE POINTS

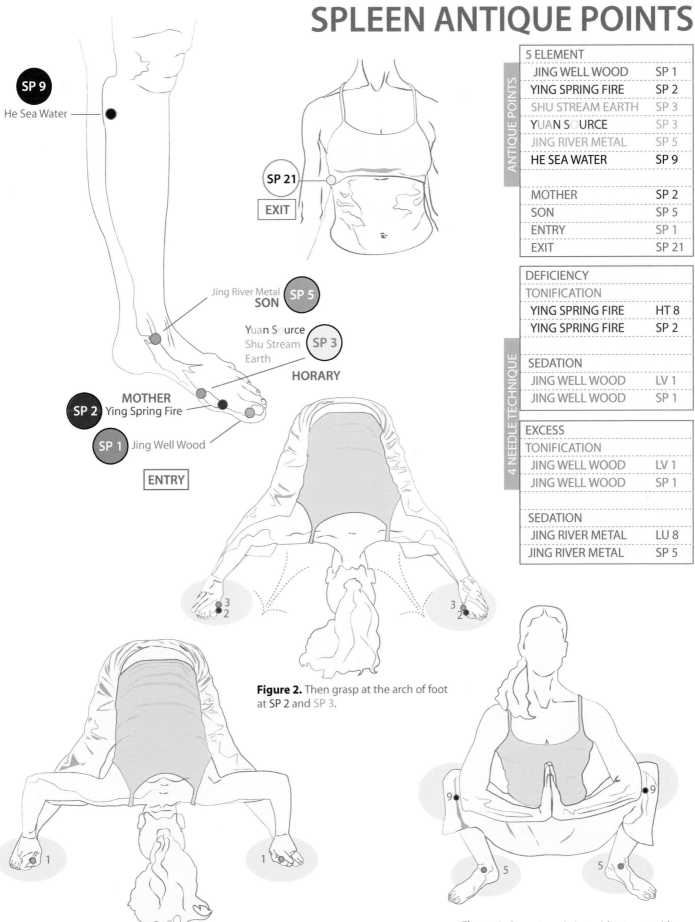

5 ELEMENT	
JING WELL WOOD	SP 1
YING SPRING FIRE	SP 2
SHU STREAM EARTH	SP 3
YUAN SOURCE	SP 3
JING RIVER METAL	SP 5
HE SEA WATER	SP 9
MOTHER	SP 2
SON	SP 5
ENTRY	SP 1
EXIT	SP 21

DEFICIENCY	
TONIFICATION	
YING SPRING FIRE	HT 8
YING SPRING FIRE	SP 2
SEDATION	
JING WELL WOOD	LV 1
JING WELL WOOD	SP 1

EXCESS	
TONIFICATION	
JING WELL WOOD	LV 1
JING WELL WOOD	SP 1
SEDATION	
JING RIVER METAL	LU 8
JING RIVER METAL	SP 5

SP 9
He Sea Water

SP 21
EXIT

Jing River Metal SP 5
SON

Yuan Source
Shu Stream SP 3
Earth
HORARY

MOTHER
SP 2 Ying Spring Fire

SP 1 Jing Well Wood

ENTRY

Figure 2. Then grasp at the arch of foot at SP 2 and SP 3.

Figure 1. With wide stance and slightly bent knees, fold forward and grasp the outside of big toe at SP 1.

Figure 3. Come to a sitting wide stance with strong ankles, balancing at the inner ankle crease at SP 5 and press elbows into SP 9.

HEART ANTIQUE POINTS

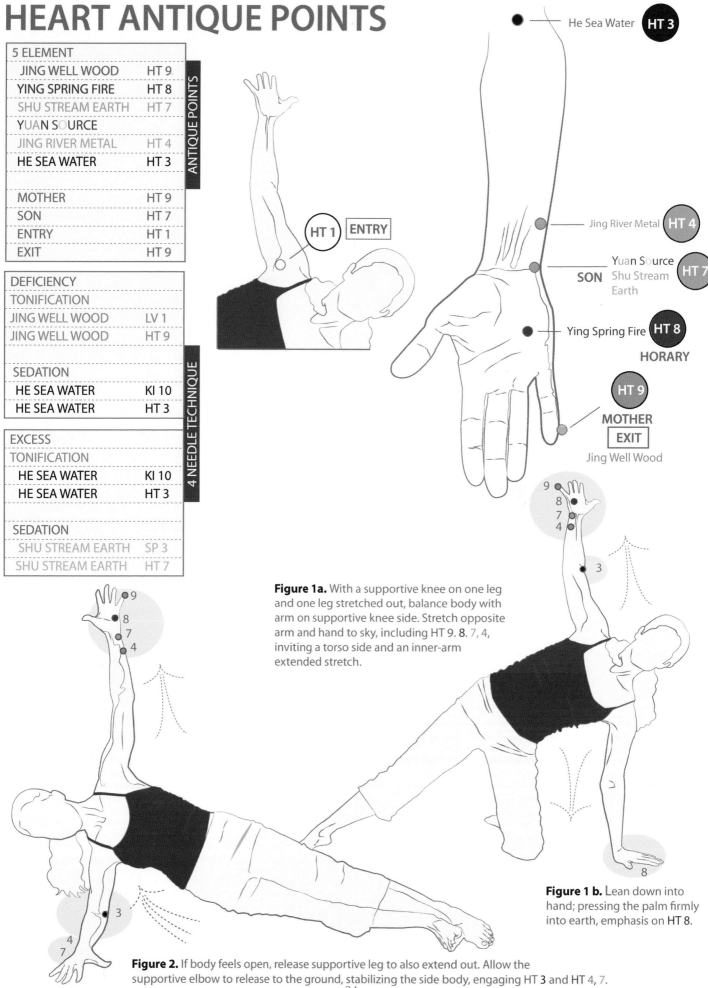

5 ELEMENT	
JING WELL WOOD	HT 9
YING SPRING FIRE	HT 8
SHU STREAM EARTH	HT 7
YUAN SOURCE	
JING RIVER METAL	HT 4
HE SEA WATER	HT 3
MOTHER	HT 9
SON	HT 7
ENTRY	HT 1
EXIT	HT 9

ANTIQUE POINTS

DEFICIENCY	
TONIFICATION	
JING WELL WOOD	LV 1
JING WELL WOOD	HT 9
SEDATION	
HE SEA WATER	KI 10
HE SEA WATER	HT 3

EXCESS	
TONIFICATION	
HE SEA WATER	KI 10
HE SEA WATER	HT 3
SEDATION	
SHU STREAM EARTH	SP 3
SHU STREAM EARTH	HT 7

4 NEEDLE TECHNIQUE

HT 3 — He Sea Water

HT 1 — ENTRY

HT 4 — Jing River Metal

HT 7 — Yuan Source / Shu Stream Earth / SON

HT 8 — Ying Spring Fire / HORARY

HT 9 — MOTHER / EXIT / Jing Well Wood

Figure 1a. With a supportive knee on one leg and one leg stretched out, balance body with arm on supportive knee side. Stretch opposite arm and hand to sky, including HT 9. 8. 7, 4, inviting a torso side and an inner-arm extended stretch.

Figure 1 b. Lean down into hand; pressing the palm firmly into earth, emphasis on HT 8.

Figure 2. If body feels open, release supportive leg to also extend out. Allow the supportive elbow to release to the ground, stabilizing the side body, engaging HT 3 and HT 4, 7.

SMALL INTESTINE ANTIQUE POINTS

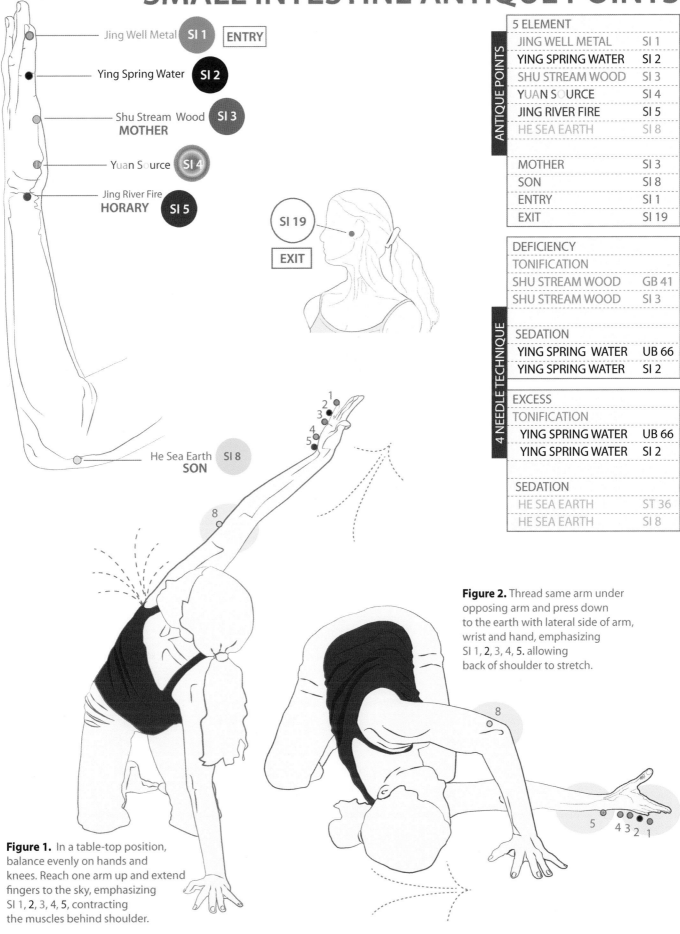

Jing Well Metal **SI 1** ENTRY

Ying Spring Water **SI 2**

Shu Stream Wood **SI 3**
MOTHER

Yuan Source **SI 4**

Jing River Fire
HORARY **SI 5**

SI 19
EXIT

He Sea Earth **SI 8**
SON

ANTIQUE POINTS	5 ELEMENT	
	JING WELL METAL	SI 1
	YING SPRING WATER	SI 2
	SHU STREAM WOOD	SI 3
	YUAN SOURCE	SI 4
	JING RIVER FIRE	SI 5
	HE SEA EARTH	SI 8
	MOTHER	SI 3
	SON	SI 8
	ENTRY	SI 1
	EXIT	SI 19

4 NEEDLE TECHNIQUE	DEFICIENCY	
	TONIFICATION	
	SHU STREAM WOOD	GB 41
	SHU STREAM WOOD	SI 3
	SEDATION	
	YING SPRING WATER	UB 66
	YING SPRING WATER	SI 2

	EXCESS	
	TONIFICATION	
	YING SPRING WATER	UB 66
	YING SPRING WATER	SI 2
	SEDATION	
	HE SEA EARTH	ST 36
	HE SEA EARTH	SI 8

Figure 2. Thread same arm under opposing arm and press down to the earth with lateral side of arm, wrist and hand, emphasizing SI 1, 2, 3, 4, 5. allowing back of shoulder to stretch.

Figure 1. In a table-top position, balance evenly on hands and knees. Reach one arm up and extend fingers to the sky, emphasizing SI 1, **2**, 3, 4, **5**, contracting the muscles behind shoulder.

URINARY BLADDER ANTIQUE POINTS

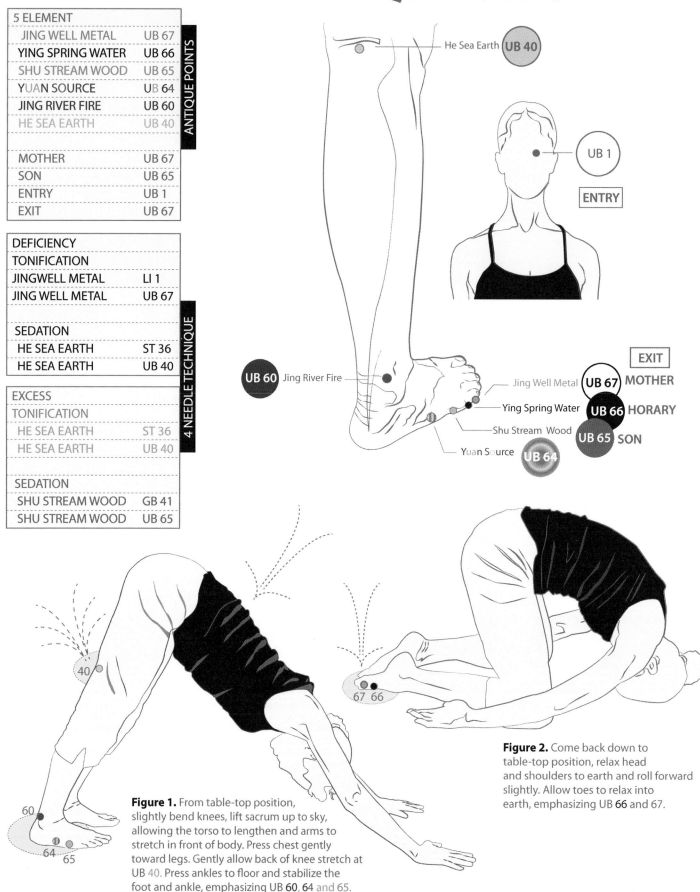

5 ELEMENT		
JING WELL METAL	UB 67	
YING SPRING WATER	UB 66	
SHU STREAM WOOD	UB 65	
YUAN SOURCE	UB 64	
JING RIVER FIRE	UB 60	
HE SEA EARTH	UB 40	
MOTHER	UB 67	
SON	UB 65	
ENTRY	UB 1	
EXIT	UB 67	

ANTIQUE POINTS

DEFICIENCY		
TONIFICATION		
JINGWELL METAL	LI 1	
JING WELL METAL	UB 67	
SEDATION		
HE SEA EARTH	ST 36	
HE SEA EARTH	UB 40	

EXCESS		
TONIFICATION		
HE SEA EARTH	ST 36	
HE SEA EARTH	UB 40	
SEDATION		
SHU STREAM WOOD	GB 41	
SHU STREAM WOOD	UB 65	

4 NEEDLE TECHNIQUE

He Sea Earth **UB 40**

UB 1

ENTRY

UB 60 Jing River Fire

EXIT

Jing Well Metal **UB 67** MOTHER

Ying Spring Water **UB 66** HORARY

Shu Stream Wood **UB 65** SON

Yuan Source **UB 64**

Figure 1. From table-top position, slightly bend knees, lift sacrum up to sky, allowing the torso to lengthen and arms to stretch in front of body. Press chest gently toward legs. Gently allow back of knee stretch at UB 40. Press ankles to floor and stabilize the foot and ankle, emphasizing UB **60**, **64** and **65**.

Figure 2. Come back down to table-top position, relax head and shoulders to earth and roll forward slightly. Allow toes to relax into earth, emphasizing UB **66** and **67**.

KIDNEY ANTIQUE POINTS

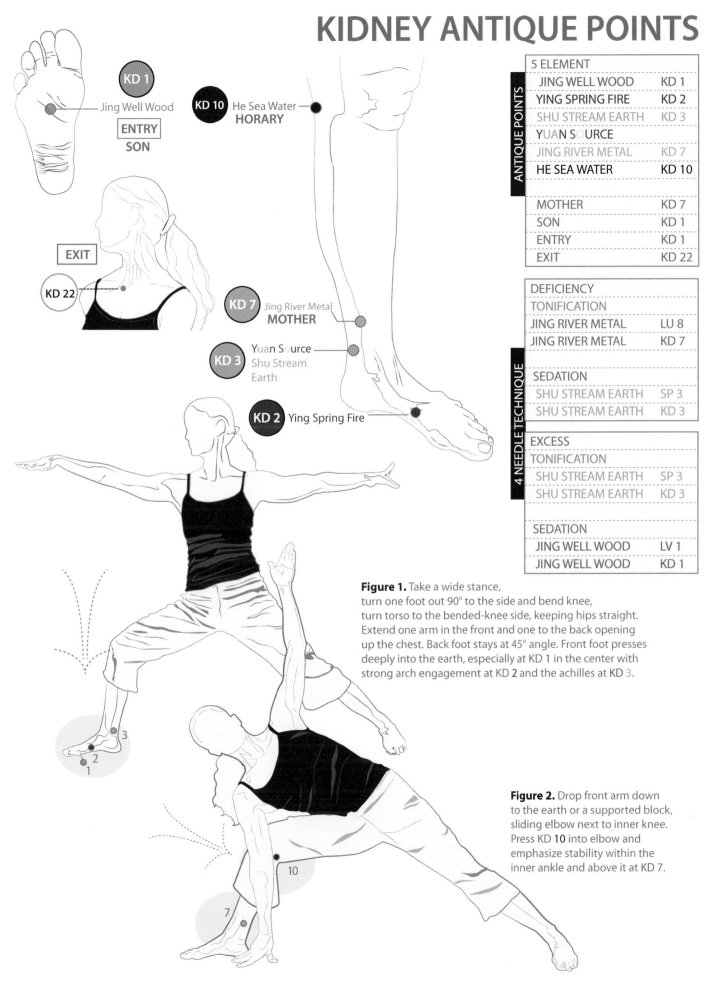

KD 1
Jing Well Wood
ENTRY
SON

KD 10 He Sea Water
HORARY

EXIT

KD 22

KD 7 Jing River Metal
MOTHER

Yuan Source
Shu Stream
Earth

KD 3

KD 2 Ying Spring Fire

ANTIQUE POINTS	5 ELEMENT		
	JING WELL WOOD	KD 1	
	YING SPRING FIRE	**KD 2**	
	SHU STREAM EARTH	KD 3	
	YUAN SOURCE		
	JING RIVER METAL	KD 7	
	HE SEA WATER	**KD 10**	
	MOTHER	KD 7	
	SON	KD 1	
	ENTRY	KD 1	
	EXIT	KD 22	

4 NEEDLE TECHNIQUE	DEFICIENCY		
	TONIFICATION		
	JING RIVER METAL	LU 8	
	JING RIVER METAL	KD 7	
	SEDATION		
	SHU STREAM EARTH	SP 3	
	SHU STREAM EARTH	KD 3	
	EXCESS		
	TONIFICATION		
	SHU STREAM EARTH	SP 3	
	SHU STREAM EARTH	KD 3	
	SEDATION		
	JING WELL WOOD	LV 1	
	JING WELL WOOD	KD 1	

Figure 1. Take a wide stance, turn one foot out 90° to the side and bend knee, turn torso to the bended-knee side, keeping hips straight. Extend one arm in the front and one to the back opening up the chest. Back foot stays at 45° angle. Front foot presses deeply into the earth, especially at KD 1 in the center with strong arch engagement at KD 2 and the achilles at KD 3.

Figure 2. Drop front arm down to the earth or a supported block, sliding elbow next to inner knee. Press KD 10 into elbow and emphasize stability within the inner ankle and above it at KD 7.

PERICARDIUM ANTIQUE POINTS

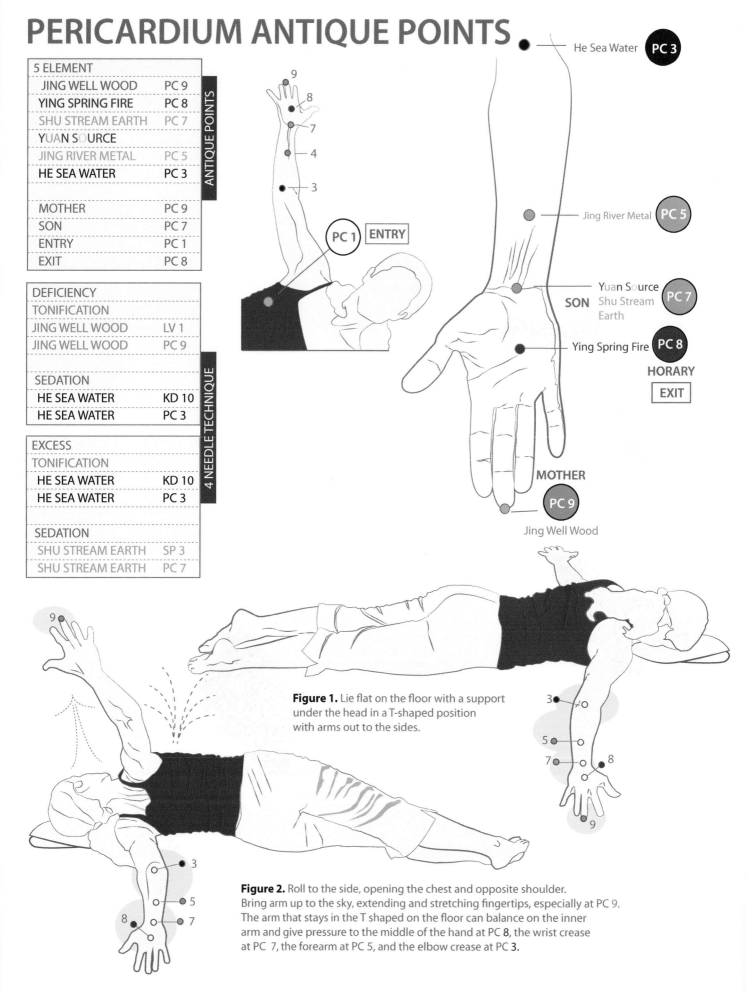

5 ELEMENT	
JING WELL WOOD	PC 9
YING SPRING FIRE	PC 8
SHU STREAM EARTH	PC 7
YUAN SOURCE	
JING RIVER METAL	PC 5
HE SEA WATER	PC 3
MOTHER	PC 9
SON	PC 7
ENTRY	PC 1
EXIT	PC 8

ANTIQUE POINTS

DEFICIENCY	
TONIFICATION	
JING WELL WOOD	LV 1
JING WELL WOOD	PC 9
SEDATION	
HE SEA WATER	KD 10
HE SEA WATER	PC 3

EXCESS	
TONIFICATION	
HE SEA WATER	KD 10
HE SEA WATER	PC 3
SEDATION	
SHU STREAM EARTH	SP 3
SHU STREAM EARTH	PC 7

4 NEEDLE TECHNIQUE

He Sea Water **PC 3**

Jing River Metal **PC 5**

Yuan Source **PC 7**
Shu Stream Earth
SON

Ying Spring Fire **PC 8**

HORARY

EXIT

MOTHER

PC 9

Jing Well Wood

PC 1 ENTRY

Figure 1. Lie flat on the floor with a support under the head in a T-shaped position with arms out to the sides.

Figure 2. Roll to the side, opening the chest and opposite shoulder. Bring arm up to the sky, extending and stretching fingertips, especially at PC 9. The arm that stays in the T shaped on the floor can balance on the inner arm and give pressure to the middle of the hand at PC 8, the wrist crease at PC 7, the forearm at PC 5, and the elbow crease at PC 3.

SAN JIAO ANTIQUE POINTS

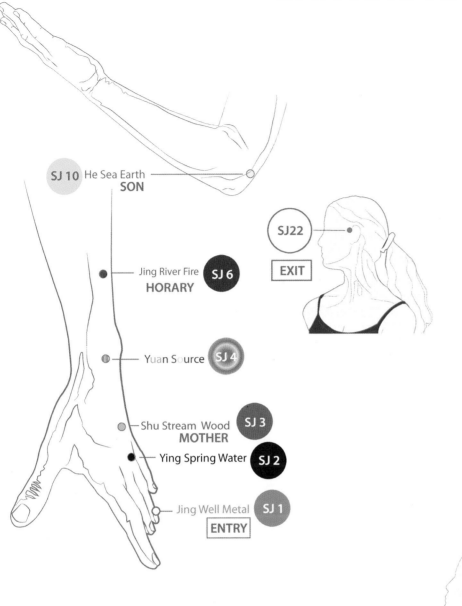

ANTIQUE POINTS

DEFICIENCY	
TONIFICATION	
SHU STREAM WOOD	GB 41
SHU STREAM WOOD	SJ 3
SEDATION	
YING SPRING WATER	UB 66
YING SPRING WATER	SJ 2

EXCESS	
TONIFICATION	
YING SPRING WATER	UB 66
YING SPRING WATER	SJ 2
SEDATION	
HE SEA EARTH	ST 36
HE SEA EARTH	SJ 10

4 NEEDLE TECHNIQUE

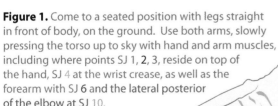

Figure 1. Come to a seated position with legs straight in front of body, on the ground. Use both arms, slowly pressing the torso up to sky with hand and arm muscles, including where points SJ 1, 2, 3, reside on top of the hand, SJ 4 at the wrist crease, as well as the forearm with SJ 6 and the lateral posterior of the elbow at SJ 10.

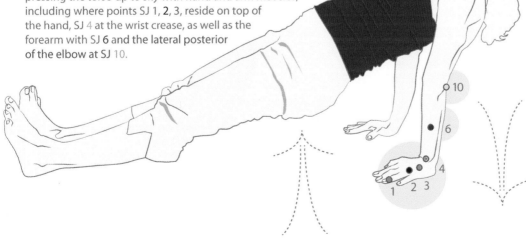

GALLBLADDER ANTIQUE POINTS

5 ELEMENT	
JING WELL METAL	GB 44
YING SPRING WATER	GB 43
SHU STREAM WOOD	GB 41
YUAN SOURCE	GB 40
JING RIVER FIRE	GB 38
HE SEA EARTH	GB 34
MOTHER	GB 43
SON	GB 38
ENTRY	GB 1
EXIT	GB 41

ANTIQUE POINTS

DEFICIENCY	
TONIFICATION	
YING SPRING WATER	UB 66
YING SPRING WATER	GB 43
SEDATION	
JING WELL METAL	LI 1
JING WELL METAL	GB 44

EXCESS	
TONIFICATION	
JING WELL METAL	LI 1
JING WELL METAL	GB 44
SEDATION	
JING RIVER FIRE	SI 5
JING RIVER FIRE	GB 38

4 NEEDLE TECHNIQUE

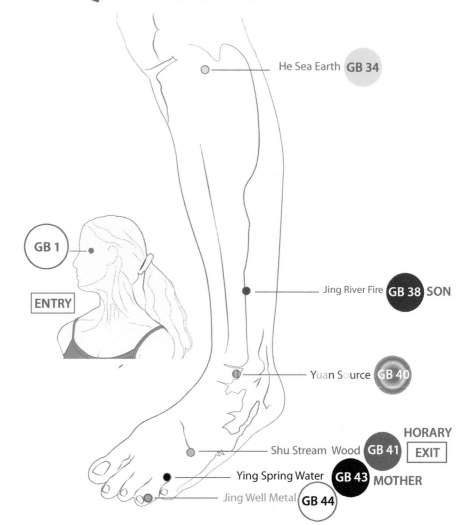

He Sea Earth **GB 34**

GB 1

ENTRY

Jing River Fire **GB 38** SON

Yuan Source **GB 40**

HORARY

Shu Stream Wood **GB 41** **EXIT**

Ying Spring Water **GB 43** MOTHER

Jing Well Metal **GB 44**

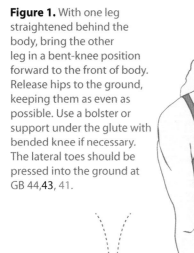

Figure 1. With one leg straightened behind the body, bring the other leg in a bent-knee position forward to the front of body. Release hips to the ground, keeping them as even as possible. Use a bolster or support under the glute with bended knee if necessary. The lateral toes should be pressed into the ground at GB 44, 43, 41.

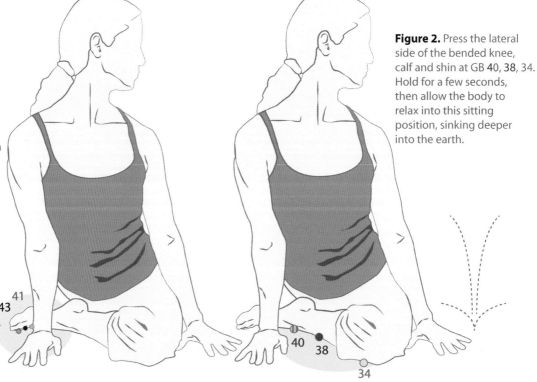

Figure 2. Press the lateral side of the bended knee, calf and shin at GB 40, 38, 34. Hold for a few seconds, then allow the body to relax into this sitting position, sinking deeper into the earth.

LIVER ANTIQUE POINTS

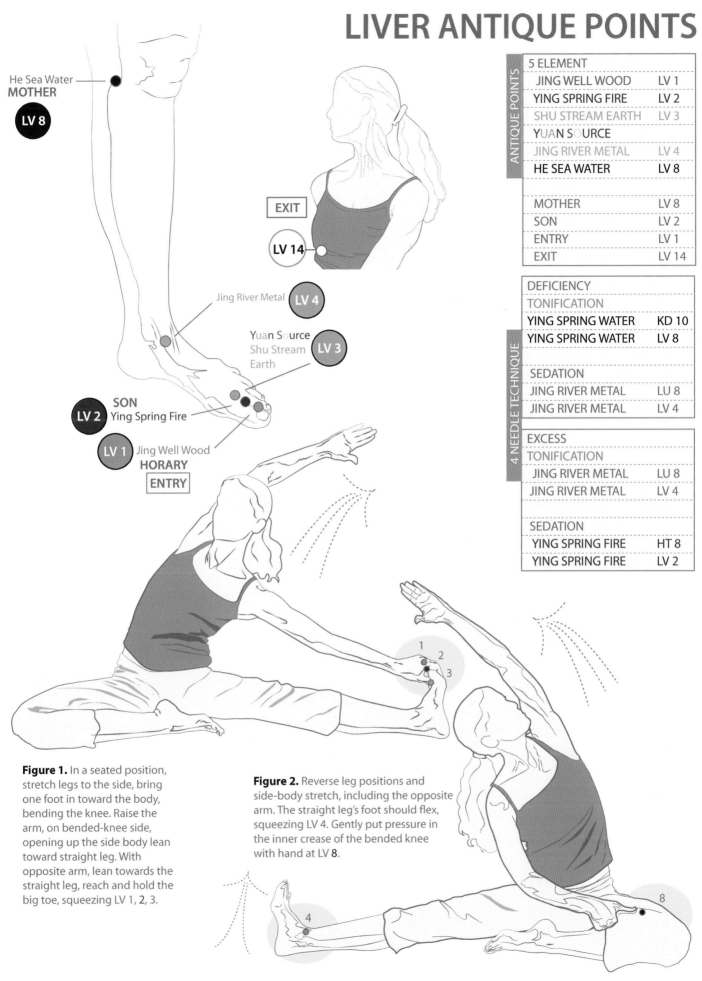

He Sea Water
MOTHER

LV 8

EXIT

LV 14

Jing River Metal **LV 4**

Yuan Source
Shu Stream
Earth **LV 3**

SON
LV 2 Ying Spring Fire

LV 1 Jing Well Wood
HORARY
ENTRY

ANTIQUE POINTS	5 ELEMENT	
	JING WELL WOOD	LV 1
	YING SPRING FIRE	LV 2
	SHU STREAM EARTH	LV 3
	YUAN SOURCE	
	JING RIVER METAL	LV 4
	HE SEA WATER	LV 8
	MOTHER	LV 8
	SON	LV 2
	ENTRY	LV 1
	EXIT	LV 14

4 NEEDLE TECHNIQUE	DEFICIENCY	
	TONIFICATION	
	YING SPRING WATER	KD 10
	YING SPRING WATER	LV 8
	SEDATION	
	JING RIVER METAL	LU 8
	JING RIVER METAL	LV 4
	EXCESS	
	TONIFICATION	
	JING RIVER METAL	LU 8
	JING RIVER METAL	LV 4
	SEDATION	
	YING SPRING FIRE	HT 8
	YING SPRING FIRE	LV 2

Figure 1. In a seated position, stretch legs to the side, bring one foot in toward the body, bending the knee. Raise the arm, on bended-knee side, opening up the side body lean toward straight leg. With opposite arm, lean towards the straight leg, reach and hold the big toe, squeezing LV 1, 2, 3.

Figure 2. Reverse leg positions and side-body stretch, including the opposite arm. The straight leg's foot should flex, squeezing LV 4. Gently put pressure in the inner crease of the bended knee with hand at LV 8.

NOTES:

EXTRAORDINARY MERIDIAN
MASTER |COUPLE POINTS

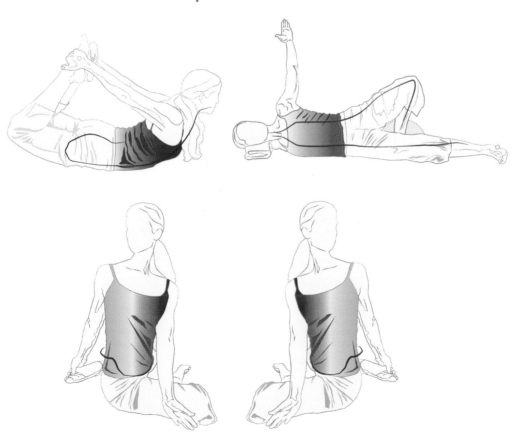

REN | CONCEPTION
EXTRAORDINARY MERIDIAN MASTER/COUPLE POINTS

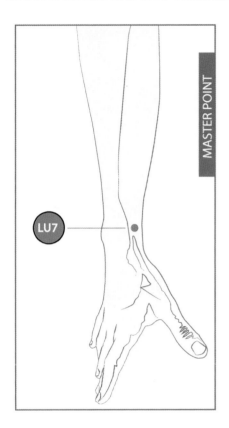

MASTER POINT

LU7

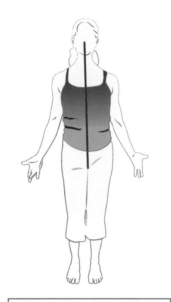

The Ren | Conception Meridian connects all yin meridians, and is known as the 'sea of the yin.' This assists balancing the qi in all the yin meridians.

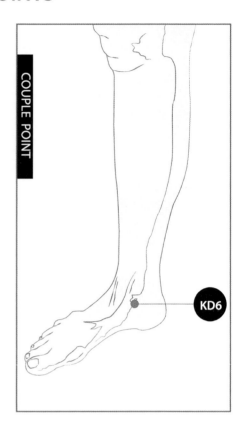

COUPLE POINT

KD6

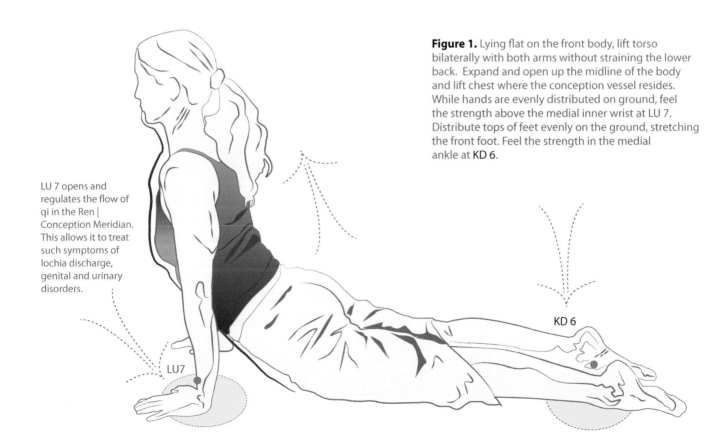

LU 7 opens and regulates the flow of qi in the Ren | Conception Meridian. This allows it to treat such symptoms of lochia discharge, genital and urinary disorders.

Figure 1. Lying flat on the front body, lift torso bilaterally with both arms without straining the lower back. Expand and open up the midline of the body and lift chest where the conception vessel resides. While hands are evenly distributed on ground, feel the strength above the medial inner wrist at LU 7. Distribute tops of feet evenly on the ground, stretching the front foot. Feel the strength in the medial ankle at KD 6.

LU 7

KD 6

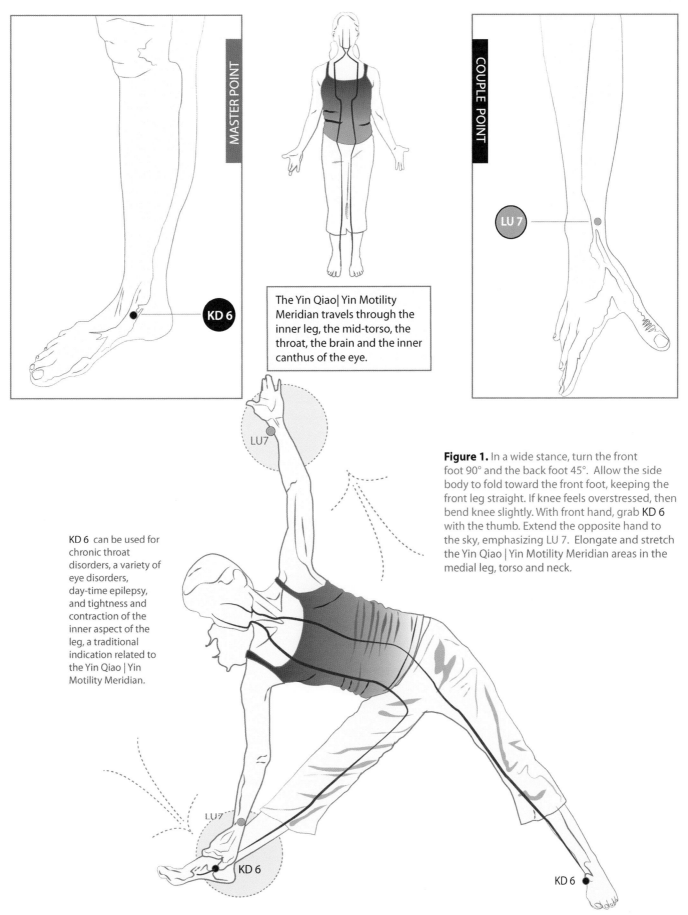

MASTER POINT

KD 6

COUPLE POINT

LU 7

The Yin Qiao| Yin Motility Meridian travels through the inner leg, the mid-torso, the throat, the brain and the inner canthus of the eye.

LU7

KD 6 can be used for chronic throat disorders, a variety of eye disorders, day-time epilepsy, and tightness and contraction of the inner aspect of the leg, a traditional indication related to the Yin Qiao | Yin Motility Meridian.

Figure 1. In a wide stance, turn the front foot 90° and the back foot 45°. Allow the side body to fold toward the front foot, keeping the front leg straight. If knee feels overstressed, then bend knee slightly. With front hand, grab KD 6 with the thumb. Extend the opposite hand to the sky, emphasizing LU 7. Elongate and stretch the Yin Qiao | Yin Motility Meridian areas in the medial leg, torso and neck.

LU7

KD 6

KD 6

DU | GOVERNING
EXTRAORDINARY MERIDIAN MASTER/COUPLE POINTS

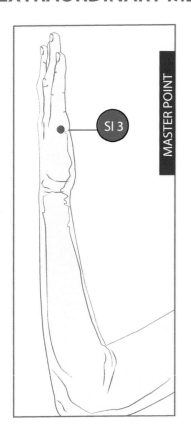

MASTER POINT

SI 3

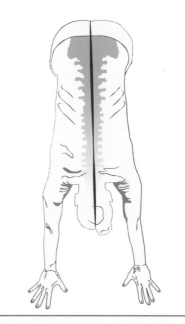

The Du | Governing Meridian travels along the spine from the coccyx to the head and brain. It governs all the yang meridians and has an effect on the exterior body, especially treating expelling exterior pathogens and febrile diseases.

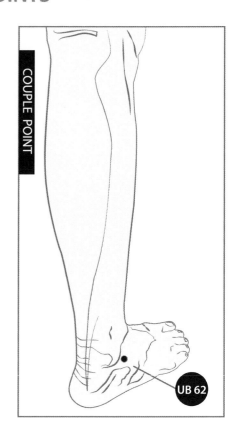

COUPLE POINT

UB 62

Figure 1. Come to all fours, on your hands and knees. Curl your spine up and pull your belly button toward your spine. Elongate and feel the stretch of your back, neck and head. Press your hands evenly into the ground, especially remembering the pinky side where SI 3 resides. Press the tops of the feet down to the ground and squeeze the lateral ankle with the pressure emphasizing UB62.

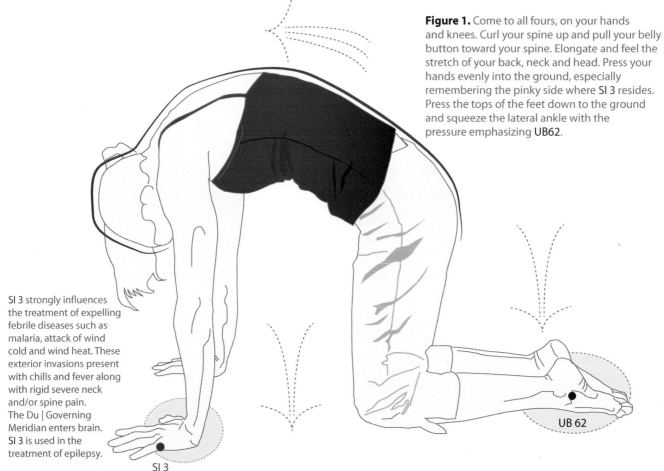

SI 3 strongly influences the treatment of expelling febrile diseases such as malaria, attack of wind cold and wind heat. These exterior invasions present with chills and fever along with rigid severe neck and/or spine pain. The Du | Governing Meridian enters brain. SI 3 is used in the treatment of epilepsy.

SI 3

UB 62

YANG QIAO | YANG MOTILITY
EXTRAORDINARY MERIDIAN **MASTER/COUPLE** POINTS

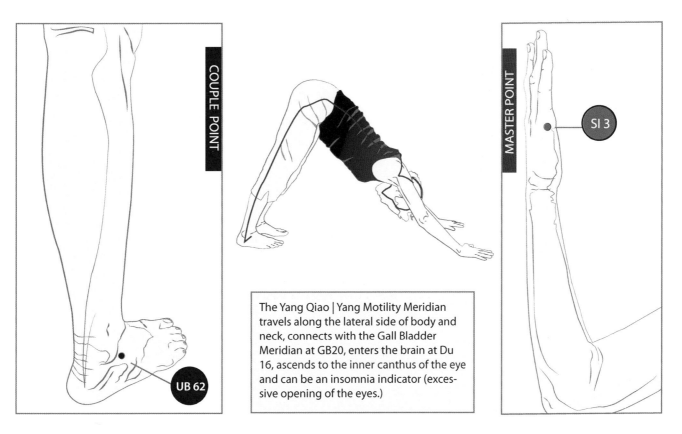

COUPLE POINT

UB 62

MASTER POINT

SI 3

The Yang Qiao | Yang Motility Meridian travels along the lateral side of body and neck, connects with the Gall Bladder Meridian at GB20, enters the brain at Du 16, ascends to the inner canthus of the eye and can be an insomnia indicator (excessive opening of the eyes.)

Figure 1. Come to all fours, on your hands and knees. Press the tops of the feet down to the ground, squeeze the lateral ankle with the pressure emphasizing UB62. Press your hands evenly into the ground, especially remembering the pinky side where SI 3 resides. Offset both feet to one side, while gazing at them, allow the lateral side body to stretch where the Yang Qiao | Yang Motility Meridian reside, and slightly contract opposing side.

UB 62 is important in treating exterior wind invasion presenting stiff neck and headache, and for interior wind ascending to the head and brain, with symptoms presenting as lockjaw, deviation of mouth and eyes, wind stroke, hemiplegia and epilepsy.

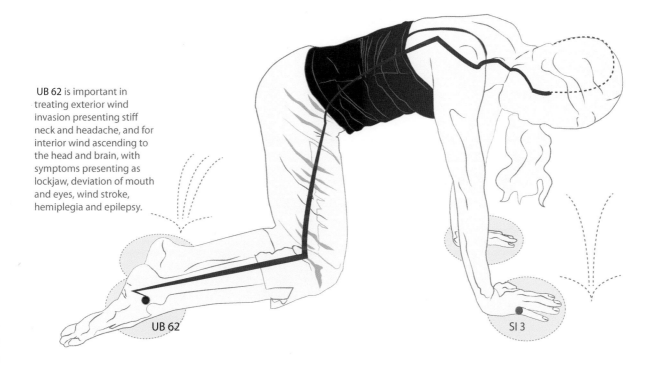

UB 62

SI 3

CHONG MAI | PENETRATING
EXTRAORDINARY MERIDIAN MASTER/COUPLE POINTS

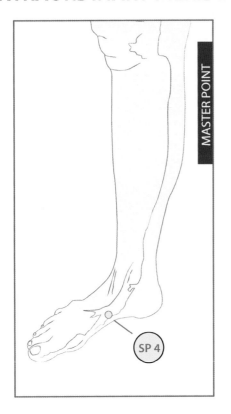

MASTER POINT

SP 4

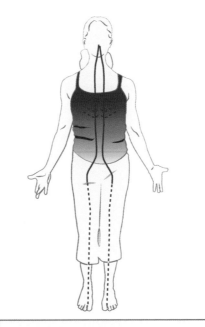

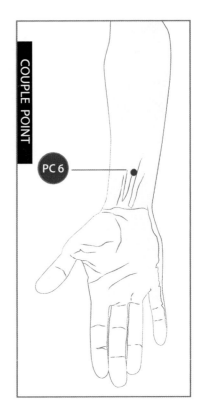

COUPLE POINT

PC 6

The Chong Mai | Penetrating Meridian originates in lower jiao (uterus in females), rises through the abdomen, stomach, and throat and ascends to the face. When diseased, counterflow qi and abdominal urgency are present.

SP 4 is indicated when symptoms of rebellious stomach qi, distention and pain of the abdomen and vomiting are occurring. It is also an important point from the classics to be used for oedema, especially in the face.

Figure 1. Lie flat upon the ground on front body. Reach behind the body and lift feet so that the hands can grasp the feet. Grasp arch of each foot at SP 4. This should create a bow in the torso, stretching and opening up where the Chong Mai | Penetrating Meridian resides. You should feel a nice stretch in the flexor muscles of the arms above the wrist at PC 6. This can also be done with one foot at a time if too challenging with two.

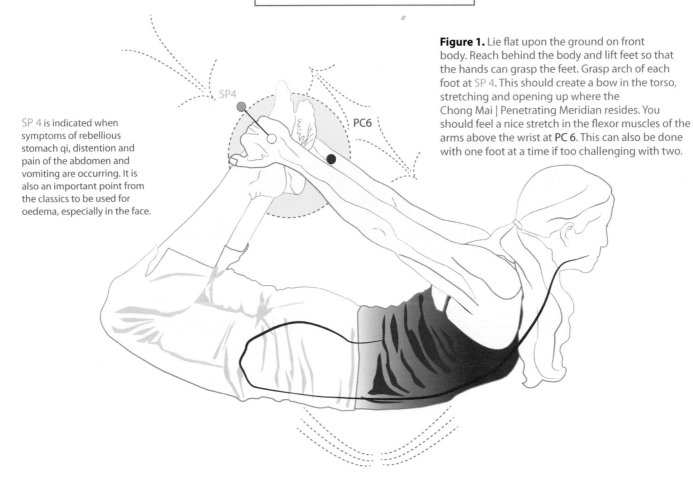

SP4

PC6

YIN WEI MAI | YIN LINKING
EXTRAORDINARY MERIDIAN **MASTER**/COUPLE POINTS

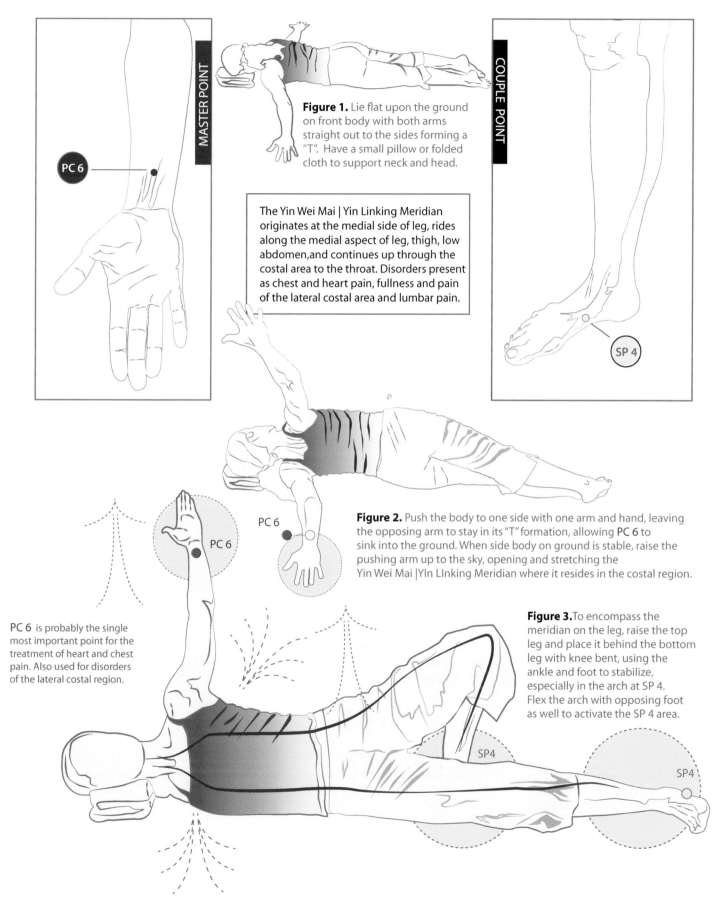

MASTER POINT

PC 6

COUPLE POINT

SP 4

Figure 1. Lie flat upon the ground on front body with both arms straight out to the sides forming a "T". Have a small pillow or folded cloth to support neck and head.

The Yin Wei Mai | Yin Linking Meridian originates at the medial side of leg, rides along the medial aspect of leg, thigh, low abdomen, and continues up through the costal area to the throat. Disorders present as chest and heart pain, fullness and pain of the lateral costal area and lumbar pain.

PC 6

PC 6

Figure 2. Push the body to one side with one arm and hand, leaving the opposing arm to stay in its "T" formation, allowing PC 6 to sink into the ground. When side body on ground is stable, raise the pushing arm up to the sky, opening and stretching the Yin Wei Mai |YIn LInking Meridian where it resides in the costal region.

PC 6 is probably the single most important point for the treatment of heart and chest pain. Also used for disorders of the lateral costal region.

Figure 3. To encompass the meridian on the leg, raise the top leg and place it behind the bottom leg with knee bent, using the ankle and foot to stabilize, especially in the arch at SP 4. Flex the arch with opposing foot as well to activate the SP 4 area.

SP4

SP4

39

DAI MAI | GIRDLING
EXTRAORDINARY MERIDIAN MASTER/COUPLE POINTS

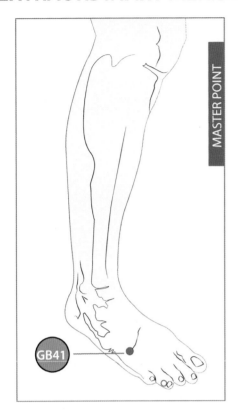

MASTER POINT

GB41

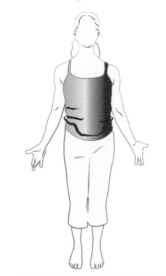

The Dai Mai | Girdling Meridian encompasses the waist and binds the Chong Mai | Penetrating and Ren |Conception Meridians as well as the Kidney, Liver and Spleen meridians with various paths of the Gall Bladder Meridian traveling through the chest region and breast.

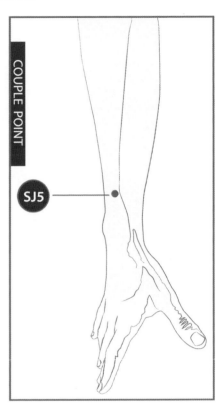

COUPLE POINT

SJ5

Figure 1. Come to a sitting position with legs crossed. Allow one leg to fall back behind the torso with knee bent. Twist torso to front leg side toward back foot. Grab the foot at GB41 to twist where the Dai Mai | Girdling belt resides in the waist. Bring the opposing arm forward using the pressure of the extensors of the forearm at SJ 5 to assist in turning the torso. Take diaphragmatic breaths and massage the organs in the abdomen.

GB 41 is indicated for distention and pain of breast, breast abscess, menstruation disorders, especially in cases of Liver qi stagnation impeding regular cycles and flow.

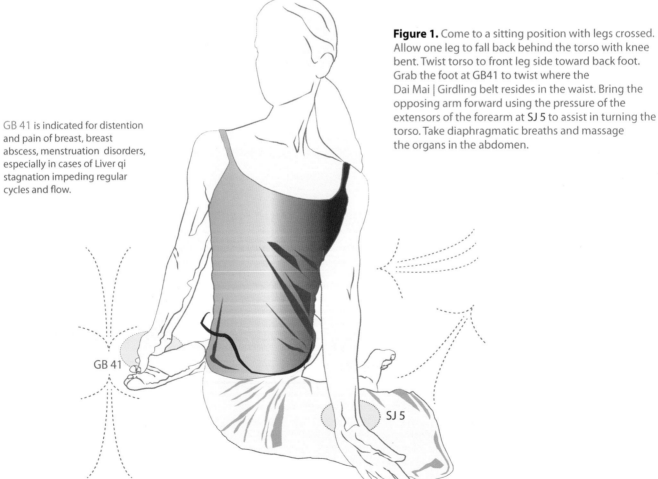

GB 41

SJ 5

YANG WEI MAI | YANG LINKING
EXTRAORDINARY MERIDIAN MASTER/COUPLE POINTS

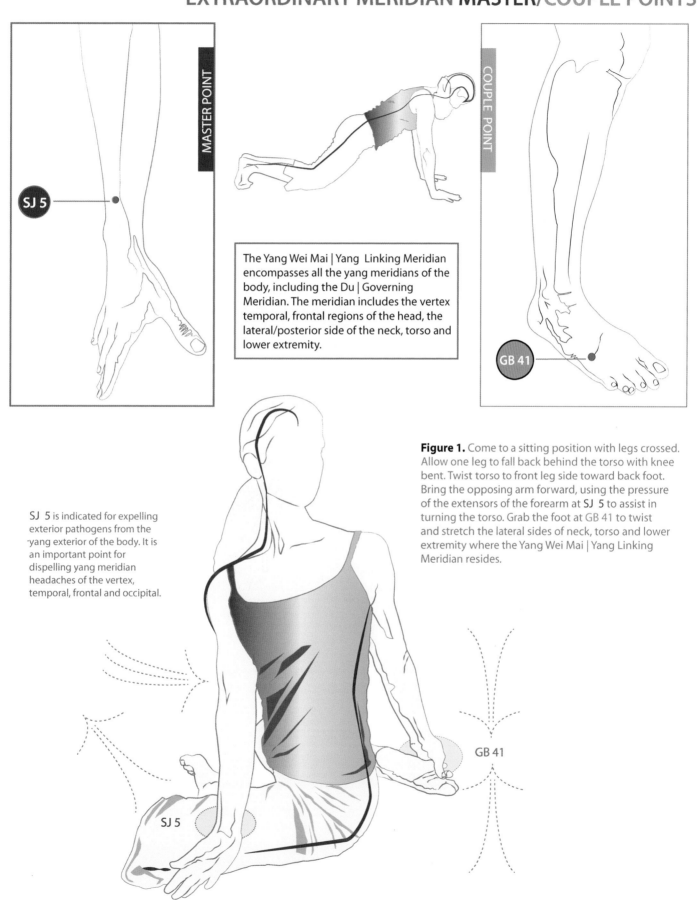

MASTER POINT

SJ 5

COUPLE POINT

GB 41

The Yang Wei Mai | Yang Linking Meridian encompasses all the yang meridians of the body, including the Du | Governing Meridian. The meridian includes the vertex temporal, frontal regions of the head, the lateral/posterior side of the neck, torso and lower extremity.

Figure 1. Come to a sitting position with legs crossed. Allow one leg to fall back behind the torso with knee bent. Twist torso to front leg side toward back foot. Bring the opposing arm forward, using the pressure of the extensors of the forearm at SJ 5 to assist in turning the torso. Grab the foot at GB 41 to twist and stretch the lateral sides of neck, torso and lower extremity where the Yang Wei Mai | Yang Linking Meridian resides.

SJ 5 is indicated for expelling exterior pathogens from the yang exterior of the body. It is an important point for dispelling yang meridian headaches of the vertex, temporal, frontal and occipital.

GB 41

SJ 5

NOTES:

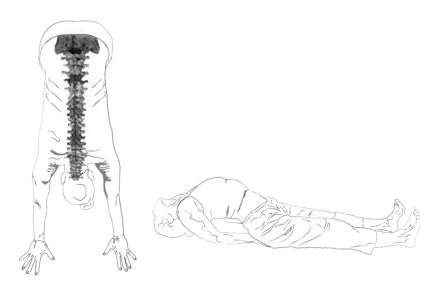

SHU | MU |LUO | XICLEFT
ACUPUNCTURE POINTS

SHU POINTS
with corresponding Du | Governing meridian points and spinous processes

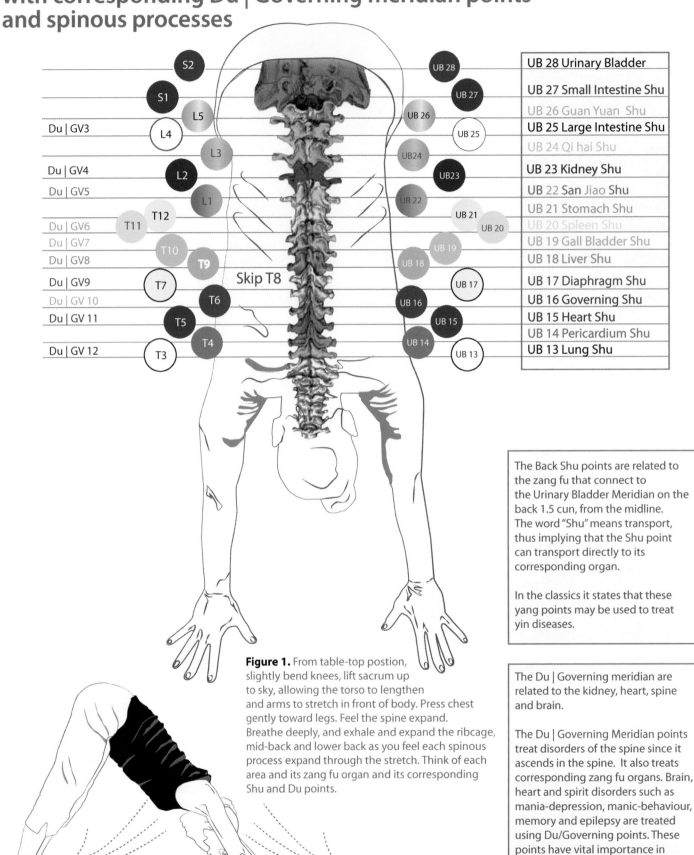

	UB 28 Urinary Bladder
	UB 27 Small Intestine Shu
	UB 26 Guan Yuan Shu
	UB 25 Large Intestine Shu
	UB 24 Qi hai Shu
	UB 23 Kidney Shu
	UB 22 San Jiao Shu
	UB 21 Stomach Shu
	UB 20 Spleen Shu
	UB 19 Gall Bladder Shu
	UB 18 Liver Shu
	UB 17 Diaphragm Shu
	UB 16 Governing Shu
	UB 15 Heart Shu
	UB 14 Pericardium Shu
	UB 13 Lung Shu

Du | GV3
Du | GV4
Du | GV5
Du | GV6
Du | GV7
Du | GV8
Du | GV9
Du | GV 10
Du | GV 11
Du | GV 12

Skip T8

Figure 1. From table-top postion, slightly bend knees, lift sacrum up to sky, allowing the torso to lengthen and arms to stretch in front of body. Press chest gently toward legs. Feel the spine expand. Breathe deeply, and exhale and expand the ribcage, mid-back and lower back as you feel each spinous process expand through the stretch. Think of each area and its zang fu organ and its corresponding Shu and Du points.

The Back Shu points are related to the zang fu that connect to the Urinary Bladder Meridian on the back 1.5 cun, from the midline. The word "Shu" means transport, thus implying that the Shu point can transport directly to its corresponding organ.

In the classics it states that these yang points may be used to treat yin diseases.

The Du | Governing meridian are related to the kidney, heart, spine and brain.

The Du | Governing Meridian points treat disorders of the spine since it ascends in the spine. It also treats corresponding zang fu organs. Brain, heart and spirit disorders such as mania-depression, manic-behaviour, memory and epilepsy are treated using Du/Governing points. These points have vital importance in treating exterior and interior wind.

MU POINTS

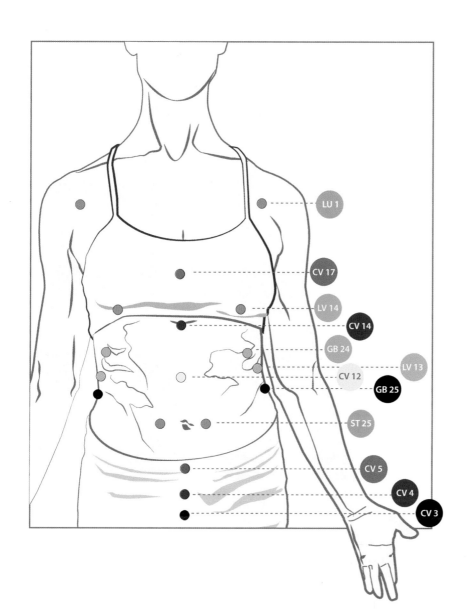

Lung	LU 1
Pericardium	CV 17
Liver	LV 14
Heart	CV 14
Gall Bladder	GB 24
Stomach	CV 12
Spleen	LV 13
Kidney	GB 25
Large Intestine	ST 25
San Jiao	CV 5
Small Intestine	CV 4
Urinary Bladder	CV 3

The Mu points are related to the meridians that connect to the front of the body relatively close to their corresponding zang or fu organ.

The word "Mu" means to collect or gather. In the classics, it states that the mu points are situated in the yin region and can be used to treat yang diseases.

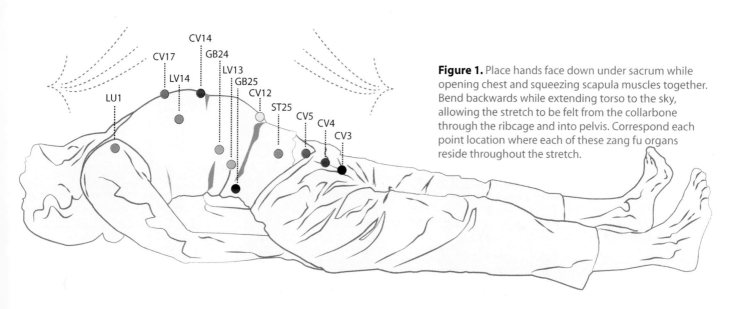

Figure 1. Place hands face down under sacrum while opening chest and squeezing scapula muscles together. Bend backwards while extending torso to the sky, allowing the stretch to be felt from the collarbone through the ribcage and into pelvis. Correspond each point location where each of these zang fu organs reside throughout the stretch.

XI-CLEFT | ACCUMULATION POINTS

Lung	LU 6
Large Intestine	LI 7
Stomach	ST 34
Spleen	SP 8
Heart	HT 6
Pericardium	PC 4
Urinary Bladder	UB 63
Kidney	KD 5
San Jiao	SJ 7
Small Intestine	SI 6
Liver	LV 6
Gall Bladder	GB 36
Yin Qiao	KD 8
Yang Qiao	UB 59
Yin Wei	KD 9
Yang Wei	GB 35

The Xi-Cleft | Accumulation points are referred to as an opening, hole or crevice. This is where the qi and blood flow superficially in the meridians. These points are generally used to treat acute conditions and pain. The yin Xi-Cleft | Accumulation points are known to treat disorders of the blood.

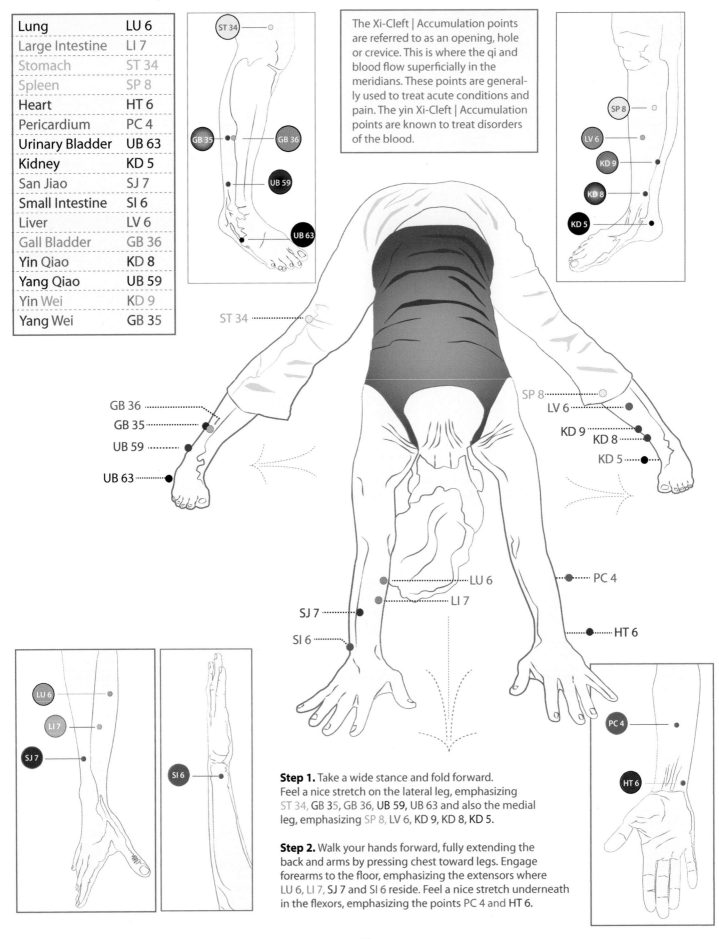

Step 1. Take a wide stance and fold forward. Feel a nice stretch on the lateral leg, emphasizing ST 34, GB 35, GB 36, UB 59, UB 63 and also the medial leg, emphasizing SP 8, LV 6, KD 9, KD 8, KD 5.

Step 2. Walk your hands forward, fully extending the back and arms by pressing chest toward legs. Engage forearms to the floor, emphasizing the extensors where LU 6, LI 7, SJ 7 and SI 6 reside. Feel a nice stretch underneath in the flexors, emphasizing the points PC 4 and HT 6.

LUO CONNECTING POINTS

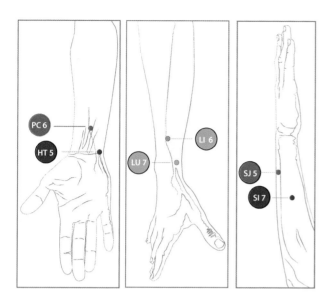

There is a Luo-Connecting Meridian that branches off each of the primary meridians from its luo-connecting point and connects to its paired zang-fu meridian. These points are generally categorized in treating disorders of their interior/exterior paired zang-fu meridian, disorders of their locality and disorders of psycho-emotional symptoms.

Lung	LU 7
Large Intestine	LI 6
Stomach	ST 40
Spleen	SP 4
Heart	HT 5
Pericardium	PC 6
Urinary Bladder	UB 58
Kidney	KD 4
San Jiao	SJ 5
Small Intestine	SI 7
Liver	LV 5
Gall Bladder	GB 37
Conception	CV 15
Governing	GV 1
Great Luo	SP 21

Step 1. Place feet together. Come to a sitting position, lowering GV 1, engaging strength in the ankles and lower shins for balance, especially in ST 40, UB 58, GB 37, LV 5, KD 4, and SP 4.

Step 2. Place hands together, engaging the forearms. Twist the body, rotating the rib cage with SP 21 turned to sky and CV 14 facing hands. Balance elbow on knee, pressing palms and forearms tightly, especially at SI 7, SJ 5, PC 6, HT 5, LI 6 and Lu 7.

Step 3. To balance both sides, repeat on opposite side.

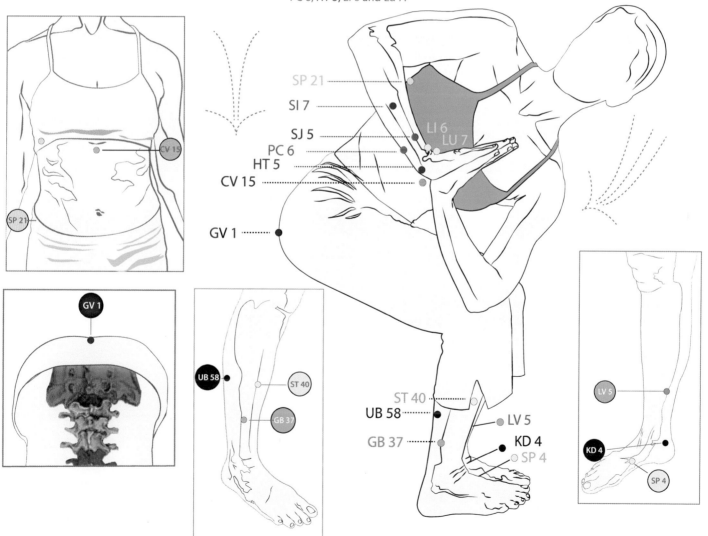

NOTES:

IMPORTANT ACUPUNCTURE POINT CATEGORIES

FOUR GATES POINTS

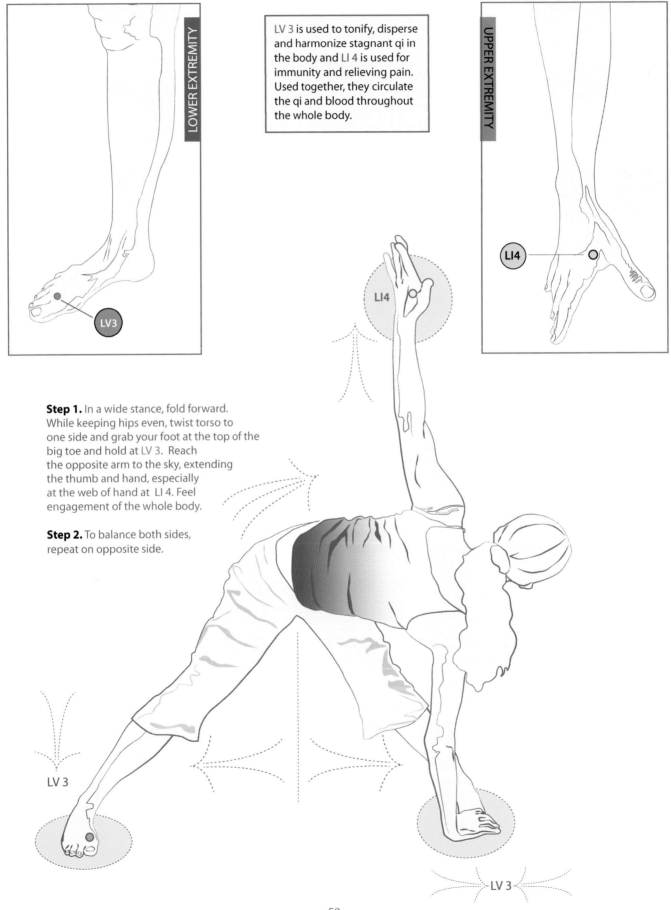

LOWER EXTREMITY

LV3

LV 3 is used to tonify, disperse and harmonize stagnant qi in the body and LI 4 is used for immunity and relieving pain. Used together, they circulate the qi and blood throughout the whole body.

UPPER EXTREMITY

LI4

LI4

Step 1. In a wide stance, fold forward. While keeping hips even, twist torso to one side and grab your foot at the top of the big toe and hold at LV 3. Reach the opposite arm to the sky, extending the thumb and hand, especially at the web of hand at LI 4. Feel engagement of the whole body.

Step 2. To balance both sides, repeat on opposite side.

LV 3

LV 3

3 YIN OF ARM

PC 5: 3 Yin of Arm would be a meeting point that encompasses Lung, Pericardium and Heart Meridians.

PC5

3 YANG OF ARM

SJ 8: 3 Yang of Arm would be a meeting point that encompasses Large Intestine, Small Intestine and San Jiao Meridians.

SJ8

SJ8
PC5

3 YIN OF LEG

SP 6: 3 Yin of Leg would be a meeting point that encompasses Spleen, Kidney and Liver Meridians.

SP6

3 YANG OF LEG

GB 38: Yang of Leg would be a meeting point that encompasses Gall Bladder, Urinary Bladder and Stomach Meridians.

GB39

GB 39

SP6

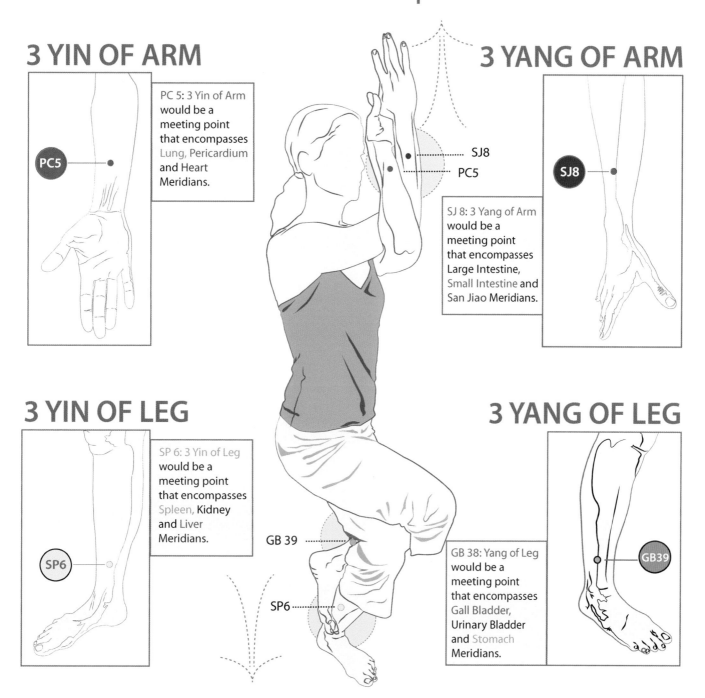

Step 1. Begin with one foot planted firmly on the ground and find your balance. Bend the knee slightly. We will make the grounded leg The 3 Yin of Leg, emphasizing SP 6.

Step 2. Cross the opposite leg winding around the balancing leg, ending by wrapping foot around opposite ankle. The winding leg will be The 3 Yang of Leg emphasizing GB39.

Step 3. Wrap the arm on the same side of your 3 Yin of Leg , which will be the 3 Yin of Arm, emphasizing PC 5 around the opposite arm, grasping the palm of the opposite hand. The higher hand will be your The 3 Yang of Arm emphasizing SJ 8.

Step 4. Then with The 3 Yin of Arm arm, push both arms up to the sky.

Step 5. End with unwinding arms and legs and shaking them out.

Step 6. To balance both sides, repeat on opposite side.

8 INFLUENTIAL POINTS | HUI MEETING POINTS

QI `34`

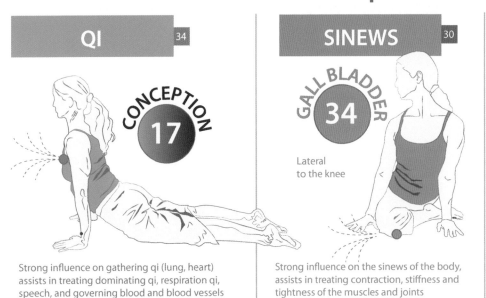

CONCEPTION 17

Strong influence on gathering qi (lung, heart) assists in treating dominating qi, respiration qi, speech, and governing blood and blood vessels

SINEWS `30`

GALL BLADDER 34

Lateral to the knee

Strong influence on the sinews of the body, assists in treating contraction, stiffness and tightness of the muscles and joints

`26` BONES

URINARY BLADDER 11

Strong influence on the bones, assists in treating various bone diseases and rigidity and pain of the neck, spine and lumbar region

ZANG `31`

LIVER 13

Strong Influence on the tonification of the spleen and all the zang organs of the body

For reference to these exercises, you can find the instruction on the corresponding page tabbed on the title box of each point. `24`

`34` FU

CONCEPTION 12

Strong Influence on the tonification of the stomach and all fu organs of the body

BLOOD `26`

URINARY BLADDER 17

Strong Influence on blood disorders coming from blood heat, blood stasis and blood deficiency

MARROW `30`

GALL BLADDER 39

Above the lateral malleolos

Strong Influence on the origin of bone marrow Indicated by weakness, flaccidity, contraction and pain of the extremities

`20` VESSELS

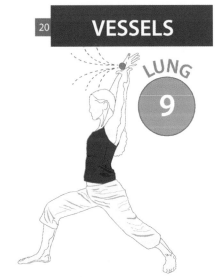

LUNG 9

Strong Influence on qi and blood flowing through the vessels indicated for disorders such as vomiting, spitting or coughing blood and pulseless syndrome

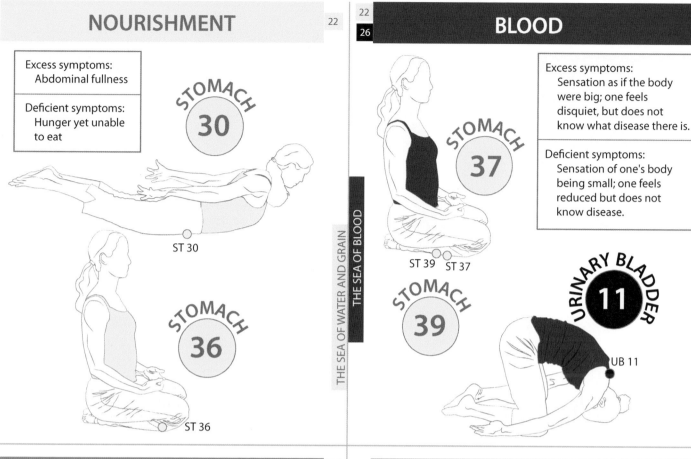

NOURISHMENT 22

Excess symptoms:
Abdominal fullness

Deficient symptoms:
Hunger yet unable to eat

STOMACH **30**

ST 30

STOMACH **36**

ST 36

22
26

BLOOD

Excess symptoms:
Sensation as if the body were big; one feels disquiet, but does not know what disease there is.

Deficient symptoms:
Sensation of one's body being small; one feels reduced but does not know disease.

STOMACH **37**

ST 39   ST 37

STOMACH **39**

URINARY BLADDER **11**

UB 11

THE SEA OF WATER AND GRAIN

THE SEA OF BLOOD

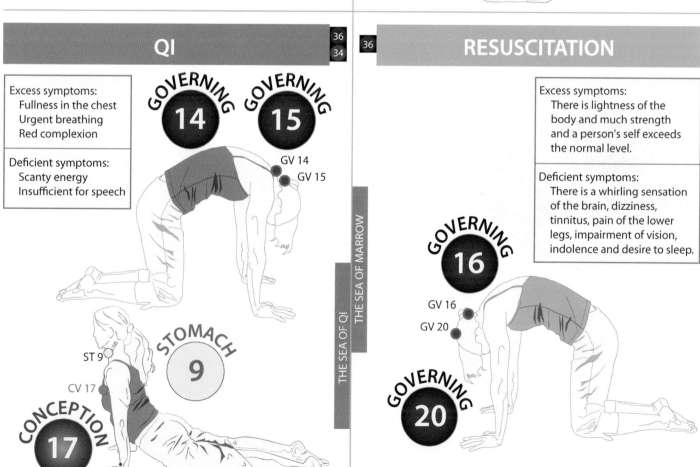

36
34

QI

Excess symptoms:
Fullness in the chest
Urgent breathing
Red complexion

Deficient symptoms:
Scanty energy
Insufficient for speech

GOVERNING **14**

GOVERNING **15**

GV 14
GV 15

ST 9

STOMACH **9**

CV 17

CONCEPTION **17**

THE SEA OF QI

36

RESUSCITATION

Excess symptoms:
There is lightness of the body and much strength and a person's self exceeds the normal level.

Deficient symptoms:
There is a whirling sensation of the brain, dizziness, tinnitus, pain of the lower legs, impairment of vision, indolence and desire to sleep.

GOVERNING **16**

GV 16
GV 20

GOVERNING **20**

THE SEA OF MARROW

COMMAND POINTS

ABDOMEN 22

STOMACH **36**

ST 36

These command points were referred to as the four command points (LI 4, ST 36, BL 40 and LU 7) because they were considered the most useful and could treat any disorder within their location: excess, deficient, hot, cold, chronic or acute. Later, PC 6 and GV 26 were added.

07 FACE AND MOUTH

LI 4

LARGE INTESTINE **4**

UPPER/LOW BACK 12

UB 40

URINARY BLADDER **40**

For reference to these exercises, you can find the instruction on the corresponding page tabbed on the title box of each point. 24

20 HEAD/BACK OF NECK

LU 7

LUNG **7**

CHEST/LATERAL COSTAL 14

PERICARDIUM **6**

PC 6

RESUSCITATION

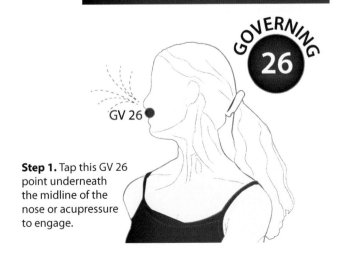

GOVERNING **26**

GV 26

Step 1. Tap this GV 26 point underneath the midline of the nose or acupressure to engage.

LARGE INTESTINE 22

ST 37

Important point for regulating the intestines and draining damp-heat, and treating intestinal disorders

There are twelve He Sea points related to the twelve Primary meridians. Additionally, there are three meridians from the upper extremities that have a lower he sea point found on the lower extremity.

For reference to these exercises, you can find the instruction on the corresponding page tabbed on the title box of each point. 24

SMALL INTESTINE 22

ST 39

Important point for disorders of intestines much like ST 37, yet used less frequently

26 SAN JIAO

UB 39

Important point for distention and fullness of the lower abdomen and constipation

INTERSECTION POINTS

For reference to these exercises, you can find the instruction on the corresponding page tabbed on the title box of each point. - - - - ▶ 24

G-MERIDIAN INTERSECTION POINTS 36 30

GOVERNING 14
ALL YANG MERIDIANS

GOVERNING 16
GV, UB, YANG WEI

GOVERNING 20
LV
Plus ALL YANG MERIDIANS

GV 14
GV 16
GV 20

GALL BLADDER 20
GB SJ
YANG WEI
YANG QIAO

GB 20

C-MERIDIAN INTERSECTION POINTS 34

In the complex travels of meridians, many of them intersect at specific points. These points can treat more than one meridian. These are a few of the important points that have this influence. These have been organized by the initial letter of the meridians to assist in the memorization. Below each one are the meridians that intersect at this location.

CONCEPTION 17
CV, SJ, SI, SP, KI, LU

CONCEPTION 12
CV, ST, SJ, SI, LU

CONCEPTION 4
CV AND 3 YIN OF LEG

CONCEPTION 3
CV AND 3 YIN OF LEG

CV 17
CV 12
CV 4
CV 3

L-MERIDIAN INTERSECTION POINTS 31 20 21

LIVER 13
LV, GB

LIVER 14
LV, SP
YIN WEI

LV13
LV14

LUNG 1
LU, SP

LU 1

LARGE INTESTINE 20
LI, ST

LI 20

SPECIAL POINTS NOT IN CLASSICAL CATEGORY

GOVERNING | DU 36

GV 15 - used to treat muteness and gate disorders

GV 4 - used to treat Kidney yang deficiency and low back pain

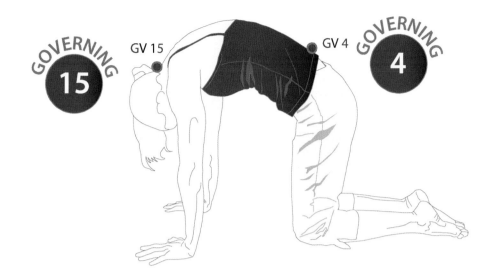

GOVERNING 15

GV 15

GV 4

GOVERNING 4

For reference to these exercises, you can find the instruction on the corresponding page tabbed on the title box of each point. 24

URINARY BLADDER 52

44 **URINARY BLADDER**

OUTER SHU POINTS

UB 43 - used to treat lung disorders and general health definition

UB 52 - used to treat low back pain and tonify Kidney

REN | CONCEPTION 34

CV 8- used to rescue the Yang Qi

CV 6- used to rescue the Sea of Source Qi

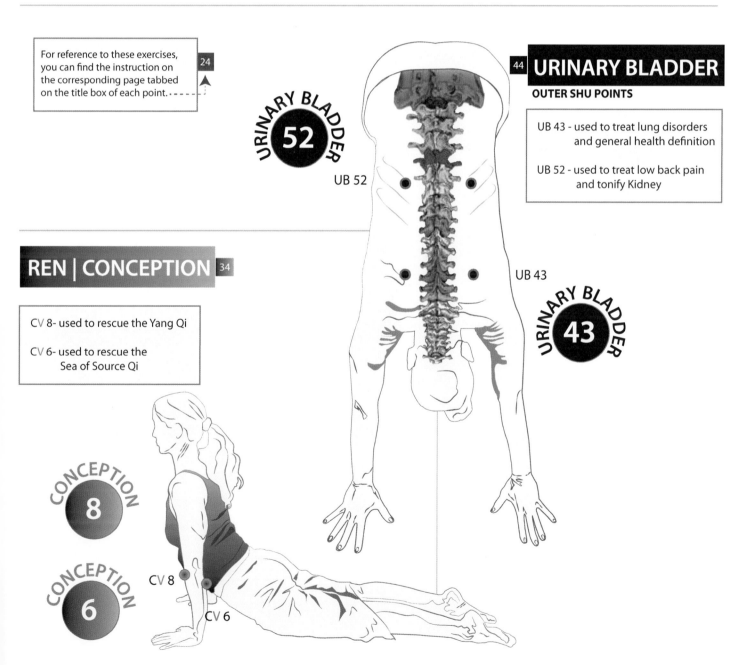

UB 52

UB 43

URINARY BLADDER 43

CONCEPTION 8

CONCEPTION 6

CV 8

CV 6

HEAVENLY STAR POINTS

ARM	
LARGE INTESTINE	4
LARGE INTESTINE	11
LUNG	7
HEART	**5**
GLUT	
GALL BLADDER	30
LEG	
GALL BLADDER	34
STOMACH	36
URINARY BLADDER 40	
URINARY BLADDER 57	
URINARY BLADDER 60	
FOOT	
STOMACH	44
LIVER	3

A physician, Ma Dan-Yang, composed the song of the Eleven Heavenly Star Points, which he considered the utmost important of all the acupuncture points. Xu Feng included this song in his writings and added LV 3 as the twelfth point.

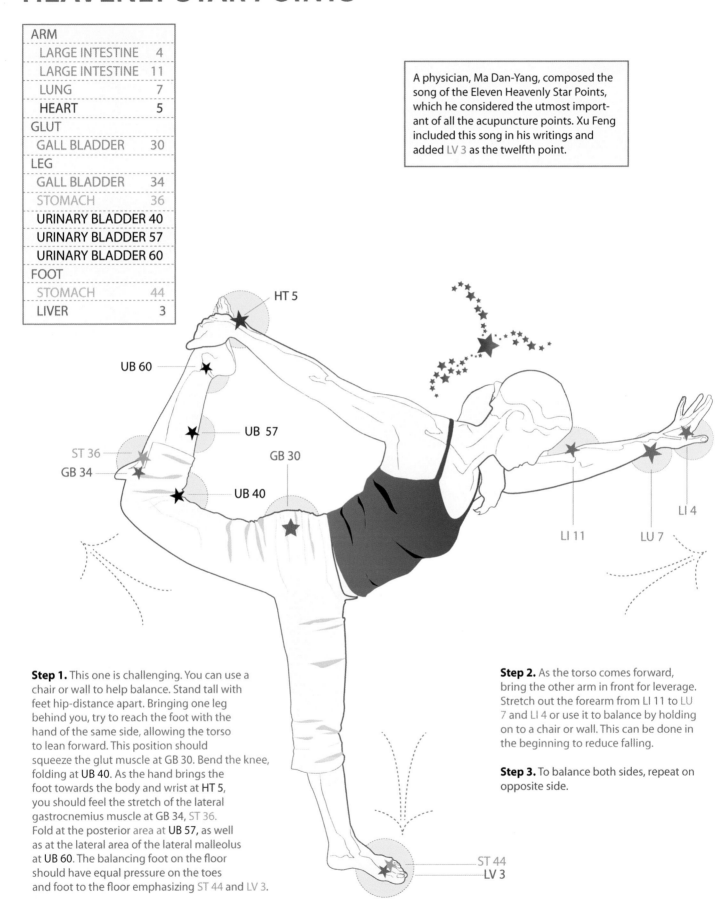

Step 1. This one is challenging. You can use a chair or wall to help balance. Stand tall with feet hip-distance apart. Bringing one leg behind you, try to reach the foot with the hand of the same side, allowing the torso to lean forward. This position should squeeze the glut muscle at GB 30. Bend the knee, folding at UB 40. As the hand brings the foot towards the body and wrist at HT 5, you should feel the stretch of the lateral gastrocnemius muscle at GB 34, ST 36. Fold at the posterior area at UB 57, as well as at the lateral area of the lateral malleolus at UB 60. The balancing foot on the floor should have equal pressure on the toes and foot to the floor emphasizing ST 44 and LV 3.

Step 2. As the torso comes forward, bring the other arm in front for leverage. Stretch out the forearm from LI 11 to LU 7 and LI 4 or use it to balance by holding on to a chair or wall. This can be done in the beginning to reduce falling.

Step 3. To balance both sides, repeat on opposite side.

WINDOW SKY POINTS

HEAD	
GOVERNING	16
URINARY BLADDER	10
NECK	
STOMACH	9
LARGE INTESTINE	18
SMALL INTESTINE	16
SMALL INTESTINE	17
SAN JIAO	16
ARM	
LUNG	3
CHEST	
CONCEPTION	22
PERICARDIUM	1

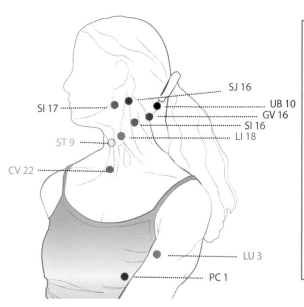

These points are referred by the *Spiritual Pivot* as the "Window of Heaven" points. They were recorded to be used for treating headaches due to rebellious yang qi, excess conditions causing fullness in the chest, obstruction of qi in the throat, sudden deafness, dimness of vision, twitching, dizziness, epilepsy, liver and lung disharmony causing rebellious blood overflow in the nose and mouth. Other commentaries refer to these points of the head and face as the great windows of high pavilion by virtue of which qi moves. They are also called the "Five Regions of the Great Window" and "Window of Sky" points.

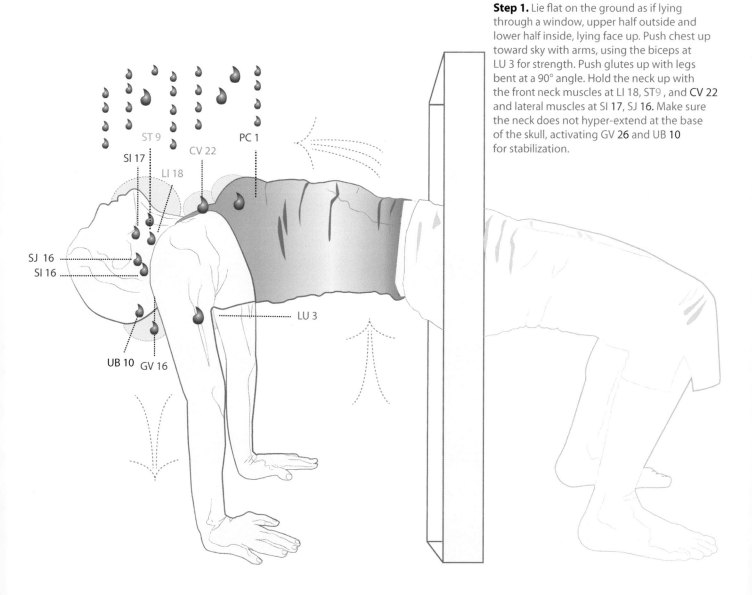

Step 1. Lie flat on the ground as if lying through a window, upper half outside and lower half inside, lying face up. Push chest up toward sky with arms, using the biceps at LU 3 for strength. Push glutes up with legs bent at a 90° angle. Hold the neck up with the front neck muscles at LI 18, ST9 , and CV 22 and lateral muscles at SI 17, SJ 16. Make sure the neck does not hyper-extend at the base of the skull, activating GV 26 and UB 10 for stabilization.

GHOST POINTS

HEAD	
GOVERNING	23
GOVERNING	26
GOVERNING	16
CONCEPTION	24
STOMACH	6
ARM	
LUNG	11
PERICARDIUM	8
PERICARDIUM	7
LARGE INTESTINE	11
PELVIS	
CONCEPTION	1
FOOT	
URINARY BLADDER 62	
SPLEEN	1

TONGUE
M-HN-37 FRENALUM

GHOST PROPERTIES
ST36 and PC5

Centuries ago, a physician named Sun Si-Miao listed these ghost points for the treatment of mania disorder and epilepsy. Through history, there has been some unclear speculation that possibly a few alternative points were used instead.

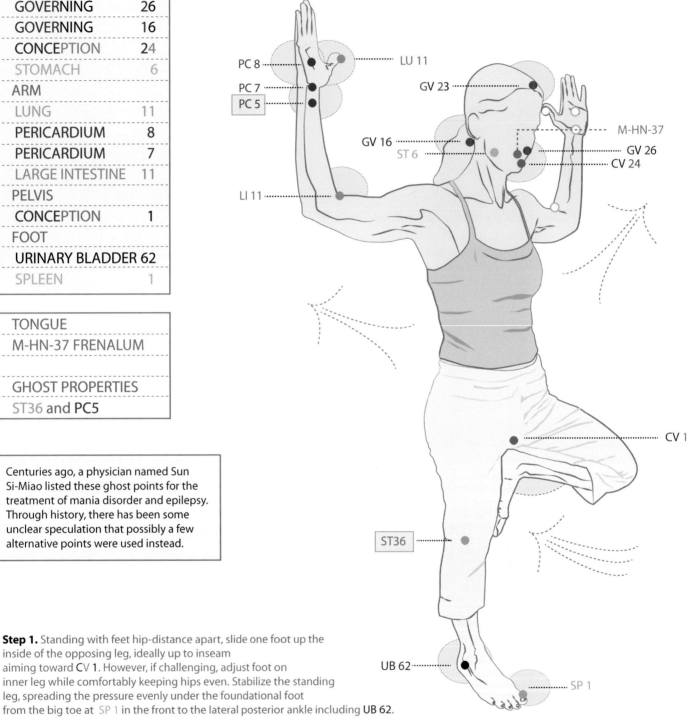

Step 1. Standing with feet hip-distance apart, slide one foot up the inside of the opposing leg, ideally up to inseam aiming toward CV 1. However, if challenging, adjust foot on inner leg while comfortably keeping hips even. Stabilize the standing leg, spreading the pressure evenly under the foundational foot from the big toe at SP 1 in the front to the lateral posterior ankle including UB 62.

Step 2. Raise arms to the sides and bend the elbow at a 90° angle at LI 11. Stretch and open hand, to the sky, emphasizing PC 7, PC 8. Elongate the neck, especially at the base of skull at GV 16 and lifting forehead toward GV 23. Relax the mouth at GV 26 and CV 24 and jaw especially at ST 6, and the tongue at M-HN-37 Frenalum.

Step 3. To balance both sides, repeat on opposite side.

NOTES:

REFERENCES

Pages 20-31 Four needle technique from:
http://www.acupuncture.com/education/theory/fourneedle.htm

Pages 6-17
Xinnong, Cheng (Chief editor). (2003). Chinese Acupuncture and Moxibustion (ISBN 7-119-05994-7)
(3rd ed.). Beijing, China: Foreign Languages Press. Page 22 Table 1 The Five Categories of Things According to the Five Elements

Paraphrased commentary and simplified illustrations based off of:
Deadman, P., Al-Khafaji, M., & Baker, K. (2001). A Manual of Acupuncture
East Sussex, England: Journal of Chinese Medicine Publications
Special thanks to Peter Deadman and www.amanualofacupuncture.com

These are the pages from A Manual of Acupuncture that have been used.
The references are in order of the pages in the handbook.

Primary Meridians and General Properties:
Page 6 Lung: Location of meridian: page 73, Paraphrased commentary: page 75
Page 7 Large Intestine: Location of meridian: page 95, Paraphrased commentary: page 99
Page 8 Stomach: Location of meridian: page 125, Paraphrased commentary: page 129
Page 9 Spleen: Location of meridian: page 177, Paraphrased commentary: page 181
Page 10 Heart: Location of meridian: page 210, Paraphrased commentary: page 211
Page 11 Small Intestine: Location of meridian: page 227, Paraphrased commentary: page 230
Page 12 Urinary Bladder: Location of meridian: page 251, Paraphrased commentary: page 256
Page 13 Kidney: Location of meridian: page 331, Paraphrased commentary: page 335
Page 14 Pericardium: Location of meridian: page 367, Paraphrased commentary: page 370
Page 15 San Jiao: Location of meridian: page 387, Paraphrased commentary: page 390
Page 16 Gall Bladder: Location of meridian: page 417, Paraphrased commentary: page 421
Page 17 Liver: Location of meridian: page 469, Paraphrased commentary: page 472

Antique Points | 5 Element Points | Five Shu Points:
Point Element Properties: page 29
Mother |Son Points: page 37
Location:
Page 20: Lung: LU 1 page 76, LU 5 page 78, LU 8 page 86, LU 9 page 87, LU 10 page 88, LU 11 page 90
Page 21: Large Intestine: LI 1 page 100, LI 2 page 101, LI 3 page 102, LI 4 page 103, LI 5 page 106, LI 11 page 112, LI 20 page 120
Page 22: Stomach: ST 1 page 130, ST 36 page 158, ST 41 page 167, ST 42 page 169, ST 43 page 170, ST 44 page 171, ST 45 page 172
Page 23: Spleen: SP 1 page 182, SP 2 page 183, SP 3 page 184, SP 5 page 188, SP 9 page 194, SP 21 page 204
Page 24: Heart: HT 1 page 212, HT 3 page 214, HT 4 page 215, HT 7 page 219, HT 8 page 221, HT 9 page 222
Page 25: Small Intestine: SI 1 page 231, SI 2 page 232, SI 3 page 233, SI 4 page 235, SI 5 page 236, SI 8 page 240, SI 19 page 247
Page 26: Urinary Bladder: UB 1 page 256, UB 40 page 299, UB 60 page 318, UB 64 page 323, UB 65/66 page 324, UB 67 page 325
Page 27: Kidney: KD 2 page 336, KD 2 page 338, KD 3 page 339, KD 7 page 346, KD 10 page 350, KD 22 page 359
Page 28: Pericardium: PC 1 page 370, PC 3 page 372, PC 5 page 375, PC 7 page 378, PC 8 page 380, PC 9 page 382
Page 29: San Jiao: SJ 1 page 391, SJ 2 page 392, SJ 4 page 395, SJ 5 page 396, SJ 6 page 398, SJ 10 page 402, SJ 22 page 411
Page 30: Gall Bladder: GB 1 page 422, GB 34 page 450, GB 38 page 455, GB 40 page 458, GB 41 page 460 , GB 43 page 462, GB 44 page 464
Page 31: Liver: LV 1 page 473, LV 2 page 474, LV 3 page 477, LV 4 page 480, LV 8 page 485, LV 14 page 490

Extraordinary Meridian Master | Couple Points:
Master | Couple Point Properties pages 45 and 46
Meridian and Master | Couple Point Location:
Page 34: Ren | Conception meridian location page 495; Master point Lu 7 location page 83, couple point KD 6 location page 344
Page 35: Yin Qiao | YIn Motility meridian location page 23; Master point point KD 6 location page 344, couple point Lu 7 location page 83
Page 36: Du | Governing meridian location page 529; Master point SI3 location page 233, couple point UB62 location page 320
Page 37: Yang Qiao | Yang Motility meridian location page 21; Master point UB62 location page 320, couple point SI3 location page 233
Page 38: Penetrating | Chong Mai meridian location page 19; Master point SP4 location page 186, couple point PC 6 location page 376
Page 39: Yin Wei Mai | Yin Linking meridian location page 25; Master point PC 6 location page 376, couple point SP4 location page 186
Page 40: Dai Mai | Girdling meridian location page 20; Master point GB41 location page 460, couple point SJ 5 location page 396
Page 41: Yang Wei Mai | Yang Linking meridian location page 24; Master point SJ 5 location page 396, couple point GB41 location page 460

Shu | Mu |Luo | Xi-cleft points:
Page 44: Shu Points properties pages 42 and 43; Locations: UB 13 page 267, UB 14 page 269, UB 15 page 270, UB 16 page 272, UB 17 page 272
UB 18 page275,UB 19 page 277, UB 20 page 278,UB 21 page 280, UB22 page 281, UB23 page 283, UB 24 page 286, UB 26 page 288,
UB 27 page 288, UB 28 page 290

Page 45: Mu Points properties pages 43-44 Locations: LU 1 page 76, CV 17 page 517, CV 14 page 514, CV 12 page 511, CV 5 page 503, CV 4 page 501, CV3 page 499 and ST 25 page 148, Liver 13 page 488, LV 14 page 491, GB 24 page 441, GB 25 page 442

Page 46: Xi-cleft | Accumulation points properties pages 38-39; Locations: Lu 6 page 82, LI 7 page 109, ST 34 page 156, SP8 page 193, HT6 page 217, PC 4 page 373, UB 63 page 322, KD 5 page 344, SJ 7 page 400, SI 6 page 237, LV 6 page 483, GB 36 page 453, KD 8 page 348, UB 59 page 317, KD 9 page 349 and GB 35 and 452

Page 47: Luo Connecting Points properties page 40 and 41; Locations: LU 7 page 83, LI 6 page 108, ST 40 page 165, SP4 page 165, HT 5 page 216, PC 6 page 376, UB 58 page 316, KD 4 page 343, SJ 5 page 238, LV 5 page 482, GB 37 page 454, GV 1 page 534, SP 21 page 204

Important Acupuncture Point Categories:

Page 50: Four Gates: LI 4 page 103, LV 3 page 477

Page 51: Great | Group Luo Points: 3 Yin of Arm: PC 5 page 374/375 3 Yang of Arm: SJ 8 page 401, 3 Yin of Leg: SP 6 page 189, 3 Yang of Leg: GB 39 page 457

Page 52: 8 Influential | HUi Meeting Points
    Properties: page 44
    Location: Qi: CV 17 page 517, SInews: GB 34 page 450, Bones: UB 11page 264, Zang: Liver 13 page 488, Fu: CV 12 page 511, Blood: UB 17 page 272, Marrow: GB 39 page 456, Vessels: LU 9 page 87

Page 53: Four Seas Points:
    Properties: 47/48
    Location: Nourishment: ST 30 page 153, ST 36 page 158, Blood: ST 37 page 162, ST 39 page 164 and UB 11 page 264, Qi: GV|DU 14 page 545, GV|DU 15 page 546, CV 17 page 517, and ST 9 page 137, Resuscitation: GV|DU 16 page 548, GV|DU 20 page 552

Page 54: Command Points:
    Properties: page 47
    Locations: Abdomen: ST 36 page 158, Face and Neck: LI 4 page 103, Upper/Lower Back UB 40 page 299, Head/Back of Neck: LU 7 page 83, Chest/Lateral Costal: PC 6 page 376, Resuscitation: GV |DU 26 page 559

Page 55: Lower He Sea Points:
    Properties: page 36
    Locations: Large Intestine: ST 37 page 162, Small Intestine St 39 page 164, San Jiao UB 39 page 298

Page 56: Intersection Points:
    Properties: page 52 and 53
    Locations: G Meridian Intersection Points: GV|DU 14 page 545, GV|DU 16 page 548, GV|DU 20 page 552, GB 20 page 436
    C Meridian Intersection Points: CV 17 page 517, CV 12 page 511, CV 4 page 501, and CV3 page 499
    L Meridian Intersection Points: Liver 13 page 488, LV 14 page 491, LU 1 page 76, and LI 20 page 120

Page 57: Special Points in Classical Category
    Locations: GV|DU 15 page 546, GV|DU 4 page 537, UB 52 page 310, UB 43 page 303, CV 8 page 507, CV 6 page 505

Page 58: Heavenly Star Points:
    Properties: page 46
    Locations: LI 4 page 103, LI 11 page 112, LU 7 page 83, HT 5 page 216, GB 30 page 447, ST 36 page 158, UB 40 page 299, UB 57 page 314, UB 60 page 318, ST 44 page 171, and LV 3 page 477

Page 59: Window Sky Points:
    Properties: page 48/49
    Locations: GV|DU 16 page 548, UB 10 page 263, ST 9 page 137, LI 18 page 118, SI 16 page 245, SI 17 page 245, SJ 16 page 407 LU 3 page 78, CV 22 page 522, PC 1 page 370

Page 60: Ghost Points:
    Properties: page 50/51
    Locations: GV|DU 23 page 556, GV |DU 26 page 559, GV|DU 16 page 548, CV 24 page 524, ST 6 page 134, LU 11 page 90, PC 7 page 378, PC 8 page 380, LI 11 page 112, CV 1 page 497, UB62 location page 320, SP 1 page 182, M-HN-37 page 572 PC 5 page 37, and ST 36 page 158

Printed in Great Britain
by Amazon

42950003R00039